Maths skills for Science sorted — by CGP!

Love it or loathe it, Maths is a big deal in the 9-1 GCSE Science exams...
but it's not a problem. Here at CGP, we reckon Maths isn't so tough.

In this book, we've broken down all the Maths you'll need into easy-to-follow
worked examples, with plenty of practice questions to try out for yourself.
You won't need to be a rocket scientist*.

Better still, it's great for all 9-1 Science GCSEs (and Edexcel International
GCSE Science), whether you're studying at Higher or Foundation Level.

CGP — still the best! ☺

Our sole aim here at CGP is to produce the highest quality books —
carefully written, immaculately presented and dangerously close to being funny.

Then we work our socks off to get them out to you
— at the cheapest possible prices.

*Although it might help you on your way to becoming a rocket scientist later in life.

Contents

Section 4 — Algebra

Section 5 — Geometry and Angles

Published by CGP

Editors:
Katherine Faudemer, Rachel Kordan, Sarah Pattison

ISBN: 978 1 78294 704 2

With thanks to Karen Wells and Jamie Sinclair for the proofreading.

With thanks to Ana Pungartnik for the copyright research.

Percentile growth chart on pages 56 and 57 copyright © 2009 Royal College of Paediatrics and Child Health.

Clipart from Corel®
Printed by Elanders Ltd, Newcastle upon Tyne

Based on the classic CGP style created by Richard Parsons.

How to Use This Book

- Hold the book <u>upright</u>, approximately <u>50 cm</u> from your face, ensuring that the text looks like <u>this</u>, not this.
- In case of emergency, press the two halves of the book together <u>firmly</u> in order to close.
- Before attempting to use this book, read the following <u>safety information</u>:

The maths is arranged into topics, so you can read up on exactly the skills that you want.

Some of the material in this book could only come up in the exam if you're sitting the higher exam papers. This material is marked with a stamp that looks like this.

Each topic starts with at least one example of the maths skills being used. These examples take you through the working step-by-step.

Each topic comes with its own set of questions so you can practise what you've learnt. All of the answers (and their working) are in the back of the book.

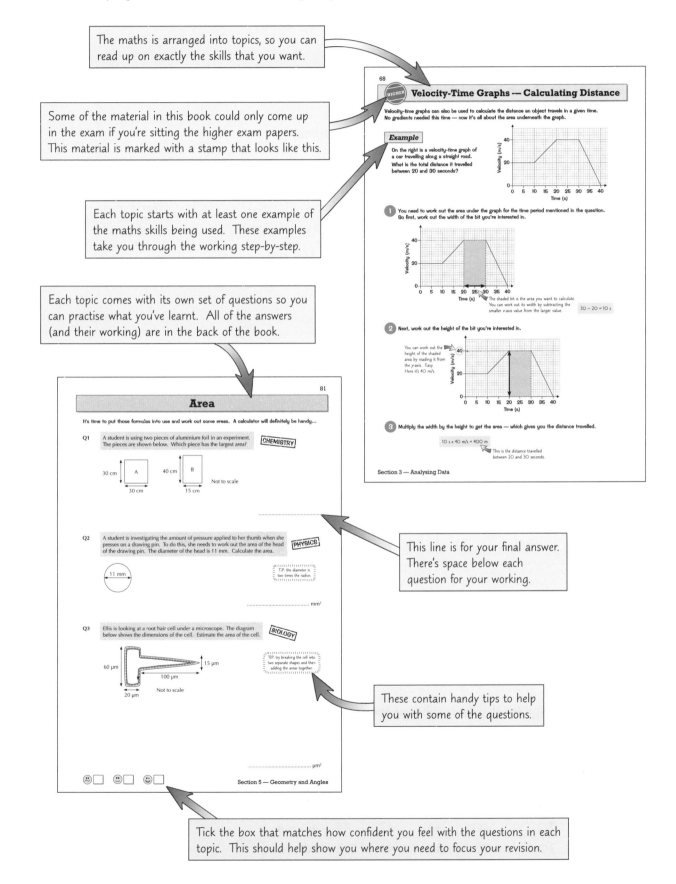

This line is for your final answer. There's space below each question for your working.

These contain handy tips to help you with some of the questions.

Tick the box that matches how confident you feel with the questions in each topic. This should help show you where you need to focus your revision.

Calculating the Mean and Range

The mean result isn't just a nasty bit of data that won't share its chips — it's the average of the results from all of the repeats of an experiment. The range is a value that tells you how spread out your data is. They both come in useful when you've got some results to analyse, so here's how you work them out.

Example

Some students were investigating the effect of temperature on the time taken for a reaction to finish. Their results are shown in the table below.

a) Calculate the mean time for each temperature.

b) Calculate the range of times for the three temperatures.

Temperature (°C)	Time taken (s)		
	Repeat 1	Repeat 2	Repeat 3
10	56	57	55
20	40	44	42
30	32	30	43

If you want some more help with reading tables, take a look at p.42.

1 To find a mean, you need to add together the results and then divide by the total number of results.

Temperature (°C)	Time taken (s)			Mean (s)
	Repeat 1	Repeat 2	Repeat 3	
10	56	57	55	$\dfrac{56 + 57 + 55}{3} = 56$
20	40	44	42	$\dfrac{40 + 44 + 42}{3} = 42$
30	32	30	43	$\dfrac{32 + 30}{2} = 31$

First, add together the results for the 3 repeats.

There are 3 results for 10 °C so you divide by 3.

You're only using 2 results here so you just need to divide by 2.

Sometimes you get a result that doesn't fit in with the rest of the repeats. These are called anomalous results. You don't include them when you're calculating the mean. Here, 43 is an anomalous result because it's much higher than 32 and 30.

2 To find the range for the data, subtract the smallest number from the biggest number.

Temperature (°C)	Time taken (s)			Range (s)
	Repeat 1	Repeat 2	Repeat 3	
10	56	57	55	57 − 55 = 2
20	40	44	42	44 − 40 = 4
30	32	30	43	32 − 30 = 2

43 is an anomalous result, so don't include it in the calculation.

Calculating the Mean and Range

Now you get a chance to practise all that. After all, it would be mean of me not to give you any questions...

Q1 John carried out an experiment to measure the resistance of two different lengths of wire. His results are below. Calculate the mean resistance and range for each wire.

Wire	Resistance (Ω)		
	Repeat 1	Repeat 2	Repeat 3
1	5	4	6
2	9	10	8

Wire 1: Mean = ... Ω, Range = ... Ω

Wire 2: Mean = ... Ω, Range = ... Ω

Q2 Nadia is testing reflex reactions by timing how long it takes each person to respond to a tap on their leg. She repeats the experiment three times. Calculate the mean and range of her results for each person.

Person	Reaction time (s)			
	Repeat 1	Repeat 2	Repeat 3	Repeat 4
A	0.04	0.08	0.05	0.07
B	0.07	0.06	0.05	0.06
C	0.05	0.04	0.04	0.07
D	0.30	0.05	0.06	0.04

Person A: Mean = ... s, Range = ... s

Person B: Mean = ... s, Range = ... s

Person C: Mean = ... s, Range = ... s

Person D: Mean = ... s, Range = ... s

Calculating the Median and Mode

The mean isn't the only type of average that you can calculate from your results. The median and mode are two more types of average, and it goes without saying that you need to be able to calculate them...

Example

Some students were calculating the R_f value of a substance. They repeated the experiment 5 times. Their results are in the table.

Calculate the median R_f value.

Repeat	1	2	3	4	5
R_f value	0.73	0.70	0.68	0.70	0.71

1 Put the data in order of size.

0.68 0.70 0.70 0.71 0.73   Double-check that you've written down all of the values.

2 Find the middle value — this is the median.

0.68 0.70 (0.70) 0.71 0.73

So the median is 0.70

Example

A student recorded the acceleration of a trolley passing through a light gate. His results are shown in the table below.

Calculate the median and mode acceleration.

Repeat	1	2	3	4	5	6
Acceleration (m/s²)	1.4	1.3	1.6	1.7	1.2	1.7

1 As before, put the data in order of size.

1.2   1.3   1.4   1.6   1.7   1.7

2 Find the middle value to work out the median.

1.2   1.3   (1.4   1.6)   1.7   1.7

This time, there are an even number of values — so there are two middle values. The median is halfway between them.

Add the two middle values together and divide by 2.

1.4 + 1.6 = 3.0
3.0 ÷ 2 = 1.5   So the median is 1.5 m/s².

3 To find the mode, look for the number that appears the most.

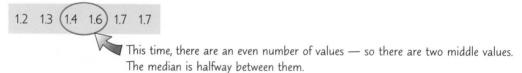

1.7 comes up twice. All of the other numbers just appear once.   So the mode of the data is 1.7 m/s².

Calculating the Median and Mode

Time to put into practice what you've just learnt...

Q1 A student counted the number of dandelions in 7 quadrats placed in her sample area. Her results are shown in the table below.

Quadrat	1	2	3	4	5	6	7
No. of dandelions	17	21	20	29	21	8	2

a) Give the mode number of dandelions.

....dandelions

b) Give the median number of dandelions.

....dandelions

Q2 In an investigation, a student is timing how long it takes for an indicator to change colour. He repeats the experiment six times. His results are shown in the table below.

Repeat	1	2	3	4	5	6
Time (s)	14	16	12	16	13	17

a) Give the mode time taken.

....s

b) Find the median of the student's results.

....s

Q3 Noah records the extension of a spring when a 2.0 N force is applied. The experiment is repeated eight times. His results are shown in the table below.

Repeat	1	2	3	4	5	6	7	8
Extension (m)	0.05	0.03	0.03	0.05	0.07	0.03	0.06	0.03

a) Give the mode extension.

....m

b) Give the median extension of the spring.

....m

Section 1 — Calculations

Using Significant Figures

Being able to round an answer to the right number of significant figures is really important. Luckily, it's not that tricky. And would you just look at that... a whole page on it below.

Example

A student carried out an experiment to investigate the change in mass of potato cylinders placed in a 0.2 mol/dm³ sugar solution for 24 hours.

She repeated the experiment three times, and calculated the mean of her results.

Her results table is shown below.

	Repeat 1	Repeat 2	Repeat 3	Mean
Change in mass (g)	3.01	3.19	2.99	3.06333...

Give the mean to an appropriate number of significant figures.

1 **Make sure you know how to count significant figures.**

The first significant figure is the first digit in a number which isn't a zero. The digits after that are numbered the 2nd, 3rd, 4th, etc. significant figures.

For numbers that start with zeros, remember that the first significant figure isn't one of those zeros. For example, the first significant figure in 0.00645 is 6.

1st   3.06333   4th... and so on
2nd   3rd

2 **Work out the number of significant figures you need to round to.**

You should give your answer to the lowest number of significant figures used in the calculation.

3.01 — 3 significant figures
3.19 — 3 significant figures
2.99 — 3 significant figures

The numbers used to calculate the mean were all given to three significant figures. So the mean also needs to be given to three significant figures.

Sometimes a question will tell you the number of significant figures to use.

3 **Round the number up or down.**

Find the third significant figure and look to the next digit to the right. If it's 5 or more, round up. If it's less than 5, round down.

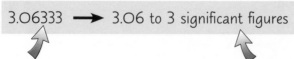

3.06333 → 3.06 to 3 significant figures

You want to round to 3 significant figures, so look at the fourth significant figure. It's less than 5, so round down.

You can write the answer like this: 3.06 (3 s.f.).

Using Significant Figures

Have a go at these questions now — hopefully a significant amount of the previous page will have stuck...

Q1 A student recorded the volume of oxygen produced in a reaction. She carried out the experiment three times and calculated the mean. Her results are shown in the table below. Give the mean to three significant figures.

	Repeat 1	Repeat 2	Repeat 3	Mean
Volume of oxygen (cm³)	24.9	26.7	23.2	24.9333...

.... cm³

Q2 The population of slugs in a habitat was estimated to be 2246. Give the population to two significant figures.

.... slugs

Q3 The density of a statue was calculated as being 7159.5 kg/m³. Give the density to three significant figures.

.... kg/m³

Q4 Tamal carried out an investigation into the rate of photosynthesis using pondweed in a test tube of water. He counted how many bubbles were given off over 1 minute. He repeated the experiment three times and calculated the mean. Give the mean to an appropriate number of significant figures.

	Repeat 1	Repeat 2	Repeat 3	Mean
Number of bubbles produced	31	26	35	30.6666...

.... bubbles

Converting Units

It's important to use the right units for measurements, especially when you're using them in a formula. That means you sometimes might need to change between units so that you're working with the right ones. This is called converting, and it involves multiplying and dividing. Here's how to do it...

Example

A scientist calculates that 180 000 joules of electrical energy are supplied to boil a kettle. Give this value as kilojoules.

1 Work out what number you need to multiply or divide by.

Look at the prefix — the bit in front of the base unit. Here, the base unit is joules and the prefix is kilo. Prefixes tell you how much bigger or smaller a unit is than the base unit. Here are some useful ones:

> Metres, seconds and amps are some more base units you might know.

prefix	mega (M)	kilo (k)	deci (d)	centi (c)	milli (m)	micro (µ)
how it compares to the base unit	1 000 000 times bigger	1000 times bigger	10 times smaller	100 times smaller	1000 times smaller	1 000 000 times smaller

A kilojoule is 1000 times bigger than a joule. So you'll need to use 1000 in your conversion.

2 Work out whether you need to multiply or divide.

To go from a bigger unit (like m) to a smaller unit (like cm), you need to multiply. To go from a smaller unit (like g) to a bigger unit (like kg), you need to divide.

A kilojoule is a bigger unit than a joule, so you need to divide.

3 Calculate the answer.

Divide the value in joules by 1000.

180 000 ÷ 1000 = 180 kilojoules

Example

A scientist calculates the length of a cell as being 0.025 mm. Give this length in µm.

1 Work out what number you need to multiply or divide by.

1 000 000 times

1 000 times

µm   mm   m

This must be 1000 times. So you'll need to use 1000 in your calculation.

2 Work out whether you need to multiply or divide.

You're going from a bigger unit (millimetres) to a smaller unit (micrometres). So you need to multiply.

3 Calculate the answer.

Multiply the value in millimetres by 1000.

0.025 × 1000 = 25 µm

Section 1 — Calculations

Converting Units

Your turn now. You'll be converted in no time.

Q1 A student measures the extension of a spring when he applies a 3 N force. His measurement is 14.2 cm. Give this measurement in metres.

PHYSICS

.... m

Q2 Zhi is carrying out a chemical reaction. She records that 24 g of product is formed in the reaction. Give this mass in milligrams.

CHEMISTRY

.... mg

Q3 A scientist is investigating the width of stomata in a species of plant. For one sample, he calculates that the average width of the stomata is 22 μm. Give this value in millimetres.

BIOLOGY

.... mm

Q4 A motor has a power of 2.2 kilowatts. What is the power rating of the motor in watts?

PHYSICS

.... W

Q5 A doctor is calculating a patient's body mass index. The patient has a mass of 75 000 g and a height of 169 cm. To do the calculation, the doctor needs the mass in kilograms and the height in metres. Convert the patient's mass and height measurements to the correct units.

BIOLOGY

.... kg, ... m

Using Standard Form

Some numbers have an annoying number of zeros if they're really big or really small. I'm talking about numbers like 0.000000000054 or 91 000 000 000 000. (Sorry, I got a bit carried away there.) Handily, writing them in 'standard form' makes them a lot easier to deal with.

Example

The radius of an atom is approximately 0.00000001 cm.
Write this measurement in standard form.

1 Make sure you know what your number needs to end up looking like.

Numbers in standard form should always look like this:

'A' must always be between 1 and 10. $A \times 10^n$ 'n' is the number of places the decimal point moves.

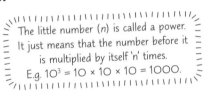
The little number (n) is called a power. It just means that the number before it is multiplied by itself 'n' times. E.g. $10^3 = 10 \times 10 \times 10 = 1000$.

2 Move the decimal point to give the smallest number you can between 1 and 10.

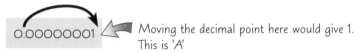

0.00000001   Moving the decimal point here would give 1. This is 'A'

3 Count the number of places the decimal point has moved. You also need to remember which way it's moved.

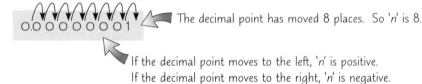

0.0 0 0 0 0 0 0 1   The decimal point has moved 8 places. So 'n' is 8.

If the decimal point moves to the left, 'n' is positive.
If the decimal point moves to the right, 'n' is negative.

Here, it moved to the right, so 'n' will be negative.

4 Put it all together into standard form.

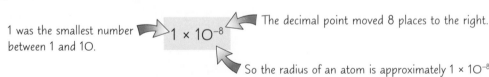

1 was the smallest number between 1 and 10. 1×10^{-8} The decimal point moved 8 places to the right.

So the radius of an atom is approximately 1×10^{-8} cm.

5 Give yourself a round of applause.

Using Standard Form

You should know the form of this by now. Have a go at this page of questions to exercise your brain cells.

Q1 Hydrochloric acid with a concentration of 0.001 mol/dm³ is used in a chemical reaction. Give the concentration of the acid in standard form. `CHEMISTRY`

.... mol/dm³

Q2 In a factory, 134 000 dm³ of a chemical are added to a reaction vessel. Write the volume using standard form. `CHEMISTRY`

TIP: When you write a number in standard form, make sure you keep the same number of significant figures.

.... dm³

Q3 A biologist measures a cell that she is viewing under a microscope. The width of the cell is 0.00125 mm. Write the width using standard form. `BIOLOGY`

.... mm

Q4 A student calculates that 3 390 000 J of energy are needed to completely boil 1.50 kg of water at 100 °C. Write 3 390 000 J in standard form. `PHYSICS`

.... J

Q5 An infrared source has a wavelength of 0.00012 m. Write this wavelength in standard form. `PHYSICS`

.... m

Writing Ratios

Ratios are used when you want to compare the number of one thing to the number of another thing.
Like the number of wombats to the number of toads. I'm always doing that.
All you need to do is write the numbers separated by a colon, and do the occasional bit of simplifying.

Example

Two dogs were bred together.
They had four puppies — 3 with long hair and 1 with short hair.
Write the ratio of puppies with long hair to puppies with short hair.

1 Write the numbers separated by a colon.

You're asked to write the ratio of puppies with long hair to puppies with short hair. So the number with long hair needs to come first. 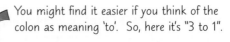 3 : 1

You might find it easier if you think of the colon as meaning 'to'. So, here it's "3 to 1".

2 Sit back and admire your beautiful ratio.

Example

A scientist estimates the surface area of a cell as 8000 μm^2 and the volume of the cell as 24 000 μm^3.
Write out the surface area to volume ratio of the cell in its simplest form.

1 Write the numbers separated by a colon.

Make sure you've got the numbers the right way around.  8000 : 24 000

2 Simplify the ratio by dividing each side by the same number.

Look for a number that both sides of the ratio will divide by to give whole numbers.

8000 and 24 000 will both divide by 8:
8000 ÷ 8 = 1000
24 000 ÷ 8 = 3000

Look to see whether it will simplify any further.

1000 and 3000 will both divide by 1000:
1000 ÷ 1000 = 1
3000 ÷ 1000 = 3

 1 : 3
There's nothing left you can divide by to give a whole number ratio.
So this is your simplified ratio.

Make sure you've still got the numbers the right way around.

Section 1 — Calculations

Writing Ratios

The ratio of example pages to question pages is pretty even here. I've done my bit, so it's time to do yours.

Q1 Two guinea pigs were bred together. One of the offspring had a smooth coat and three of the offspring had rough coats. Write the ratio of offspring with smooth coats to offspring with rough coats.

BIOLOGY

....

Q2 A transformer has 15 turns on its primary coil and 25 turns on its secondary coil. Write the ratio of turns on the primary coil to turns on the secondary coil in its simplest form.

PHYSICS

....

Q3 A molecule of glucose contains six carbon atoms, twelve hydrogen atoms and six oxygen atoms. Write the ratio of carbon atoms to hydrogen atoms and oxygen atoms in its simplest form.

CHEMISTRY

TIP: Ratios don't just have to have two numbers. You can add a third number using an extra colon.

....

Q4 A compound contains four carbon atoms, two nitrogen atoms and twelve hydrogen atoms. Write the ratio of carbon atoms to hydrogen atoms and nitrogen atoms in its simplest form.

CHEMISTRY

....

Q5 A scientist estimates the surface area of a cell as being 6000 μm^2. He estimates that its volume is 30 000 μm^3. Write the surface area to volume ratio of the cell in its simplest form.

BIOLOGY

....

Calculating Percentages and Fractions

Percentages are 100% useful. You could be asked to work one out from some data, so it's a good idea to know how to do it. Then there are fractions too. Guess what — you could be asked about those as well.

Example

Dave collected some data about the blood types of students in his class. His results are in the table opposite.

Blood type	A	B	AB	O
Number of students	20	6	1	23

What percentage of the students have blood type O?

1 Add together all of the results.

Blood type	A	B	AB	O
Number of students	20	6	1	23

20 + 6 + 1 + 23 = 50

So there are 50 students in total.

2 Read off the value of the category in the question, and divide it by the total of the results.

Blood type	A	B	AB	O
Number of students	20	6	1	23

The question asks about blood type O. The table shows that 23 students have this blood type, so divide this by the total number of students:

$23 \div 50 = 0.46$

3 Multiply that number by 100 to get the percentage.

$0.46 \times 100 = 46\%$ So 46% of the students have blood type O.

Example

Harmeet carried out a survey to investigate recycling. He asked a sample of people whether they recycle their used glass bottles and jars. His results are shown in the table.

Recycle glass?	Yes	No
Number of people	54	27

What fraction of Harmeet's sample recycle their glass bottles and jars?

1 Add together all of the results.

$54 + 27 = 81$ So there are 81 people in total.

2 Read off the value of the category in the question.

The question asks about people that do recycle. The table shows that 54 people recycle.

Recycle glass?	Yes	No
Number of people	54	27

3 Write that number as a fraction of the total results.

The total number of people goes on the bottom. $\frac{54}{81}$ The number of people that recycle glass goes on top.

4 Simplify your fraction by dividing the top and bottom by the same number.

To get the fraction as simple as possible, you might have to divide more than once.

$\frac{54}{81} \xrightarrow{\div 9} \frac{6}{9} \xrightarrow{\div 3} \frac{2}{3}$ So $\frac{2}{3}$ of the sample recycle.

Calculating Percentages and Fractions

Time for you to play with some percentages and fractions yourself.

Q1 Mike recorded the masses of different types of food molecules in a sample of food. His results are shown in the table below. What percentage of the food is protein?

Food molecules	Mass (g)
Carbohydrate	10
Protein	9
Fat	5
Other	6

.... %

Q2 A toaster transfers 180 000 J of energy electrically from the mains. 95 400 J of energy is transferred to the bread's thermal energy store. What percentage of the total energy transferred by the toaster is transferred to the bread's thermal energy store?

.... %

Q3 In a clinical trial, 96 volunteers are given a new drug. Doctors find that 27 of the volunteers suffer from side effects. Give this as a fraction of the total number of volunteers.

....

Q4 A factory is doing a life cycle assessment of one of its products. 492 g of copper are used to make the product but 36 g of this are wasted. Work out the fraction of copper wasted for each product that is made.

....

Probability

Probability is a measure of how likely something is to happen. It can be written as a fraction or a percentage. Examiners like to sneak probability into questions about genetic crosses. Being the kind person that I am, the probability of me writing a page all about probability is 100%...

Example

The genetic diagram below shows a cross between two cats with short hair.

a) Give the probability of offspring being born to these parents having short hair.

b) Predict how many out of eight offspring would have short hair.

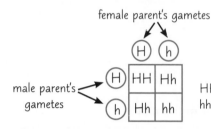

female parent's gametes

male parent's gametes

HH and Hh result in short hair.
hh results in long hair.

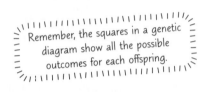
Remember, the squares in a genetic diagram show all the possible outcomes for each offspring.

First things first — part a)...

1 Count the number of ways that this event could happen.

There are three ways that the offspring could have short hair.

2 Give this as a fraction or a percentage of the total number of possible outcomes.

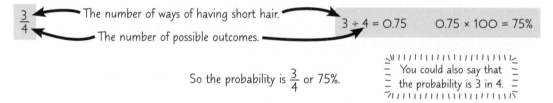

$\frac{3}{4}$ ← The number of ways of having short hair.
← The number of possible outcomes.

$3 \div 4 = 0.75$ $0.75 \times 100 = 75\%$

So the probability is $\frac{3}{4}$ or 75%.

You could also say that the probability is 3 in 4.

Now on to part b)...

1 Work out the probability of offspring having this characteristic.

From your answer to part a), you know that the probability of offspring having short hair is $\frac{3}{4}$ or 75%.

2 Work out how many of the total number of offspring that is.

If you have the probability as a fraction...

Divide the number of offspring by the bottom number of the fraction.

$8 \div 4 = 2$

If you have the probability as a percentage...

Divide the percentage by 100.

$75 \div 100 = 0.75$

Multiply that by the top number of the fraction.

$2 \times 3 = 6$ ← So, you'd expect six of the → $0.75 \times 8 = 6$
offspring to have short hair.

Probability

Your turn now. Practise your probability skills on these questions.

Q1   The genetic diagram below shows the probability of offspring being male
or female. XX produces a female and XY produces a male. What is the
probability of offspring being female? Give your answer as a percentage.

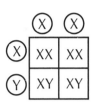

.... %

Q2   The genetic diagram below shows the probability of a child being born with
cystic fibrosis. A child that has 'ff' will have cystic fibrosis. A child with
'FF' or 'Ff' will not have cystic fibrosis. What is the probability of a child
being born with cystic fibrosis? Give your answer as a fraction.

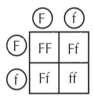

....

Q3   The genetic diagram below shows a cross between two hamsters. HH and
Hh produce short-haired offspring and hh produces long-haired offspring.

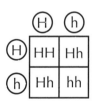

a)   What is the probability of offspring having long hair? Give your answer as a percentage.

.... %

b)   The hamsters have twelve offspring. Predict how many offspring would have long hair.

.... offspring

Section 1 — Calculations

Calculating Percentage Change

You're about to meet a nifty method for working out how much a value has changed as a percentage of the original value. And I bet you thought percentages couldn't get any more exciting...

Example

The table on the right shows how much gas is produced during a reaction at 10-second intervals.

What is the percentage change in the amount of gas produced between 10 s and 30 s?

Time (s)	0	10	20	30	40	50
Amount of gas (cm³)	0	36	45	54	60	64

1 Identify the two values that you need to use.

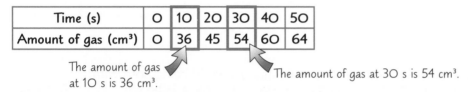

Time (s)	0	10	20	30	40	50
Amount of gas (cm³)	0	36	45	54	60	64

The amount of gas at 10 s is 36 cm³.

The amount of gas at 30 s is 54 cm³.

2 Then use this equation: $\text{percentage change} = \dfrac{\text{final value} - \text{original value}}{\text{original value}} \times 100$

The final amount of gas is 54 cm³.

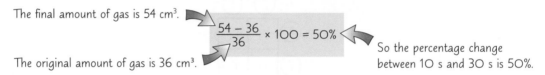

$$\frac{54 - 36}{36} \times 100 = 50\%$$

The original amount of gas is 36 cm³.

So the percentage change between 10 s and 30 s is 50%.

Example

A cylinder of potato was placed in a 0.2 mol/dm³ sugar solution for 24 hours. A second potato cylinder was placed in a 0.4 mol/dm³ solution. The masses of the cylinders before and after were recorded. The results are shown in the table.

Calculate the percentage change for each concentration and state whether it is a percentage increase or decrease.

Concentration of sugar solution (mol/dm³)	Mass before (g)	Mass after (g)
0.2	10.2	10.8
0.4	11.1	10.6

1 Use the equation above to calculate percentage change.

0.2 mol/dm³ concentration...

$$\frac{10.8 - 10.2}{10.2} \times 100 = 5.88\%$$

0.4 mol/dm³ concentration...

$$\frac{10.6 - 11.1}{11.1} \times 100 = -4.50\%$$

2 Look at the sign to see whether the percentage change is an increase or a decrease.

0.2 mol/dm³ concentration...

5.88% — The percentage change is positive. This shows it's a percentage increase.

0.4 mol/dm³ concentration...

−4.50% — The percentage change is negative. So it's a percentage decrease.

Calculating Percentage Change

If you've taken everything in from the previous page, you shouldn't have a problem with these questions.

Q1 The table below shows the mass of product formed in a reaction after certain time intervals. Work out the percentage change in the mass of product made between 10 and 20 s.

Time (s)	10	20	30
Mass (g)	11	14	17

.... %

Q2 The table below shows the change in the radioactivity of a substance over time. What is the percentage change in radioactivity between 1 and 2 hours?

Time (hours)	0	1	2	3	4
Activity (Bq)	850	212	55	12	3

.... %

Q3 Cylinders of potato were placed in different concentrations of salt solution. They were each left for 24 hours. The masses of the cylinders before and after were recorded, and the table below shows the results. Calculate the percentage change for each concentration.

Concentration of sugar solution (mol/dm³)	Mass before (g)	Mass after (g)
0.2	22.2	23.8
0.4	18.8	17.4

0.2 mol/dm³: .... %

0.4 mol/dm³: .... %

Section 1 — Calculations

Making Estimates

Estimating is a pretty useful skill to have. It's a good way to quickly check that your answers look correct. If that wasn't enough, the examiners also think you should know how to estimate the sizes of things.

Example

Jack is investigating the abundance of daisies in a field. He finds 31 daisies per m² and the area of the field is 1946 m². He works out the population size by calculating 31 × 1946 = 60 326. Use estimation to check whether his answer is correct.

1 Round the numbers to 1 significant figure so that they're easier to use.

Look at the second significant figure. It's less than 5, so round down.

31 ⟶ 30

See page 6 for more about significant figures.

Look at the second significant figure. It's 5 or more, so round up.

1946 ⟶ 2000

2 Use the rounded numbers in your calculation.

30 × 2000 = 60 000 daisies ⟵ Use the calculation in the question.

So there are approximately 60 000 daisies in the field. ⟶ 31 × 1946 = ~60 000 daisies

The '~' symbol just means approximately.

Jack's answer was close to 60 000, so it's likely to be correct.

3 Go outside and make a daisy chain.

Example

The diagram shows a plant cell. It is labelled with its width. Estimate the width of the nucleus.

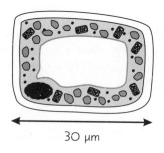

30 μm

1 Estimate the number of times the subcellular structure fits across the width of the cell.

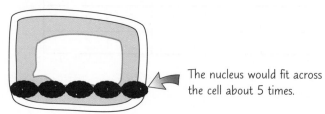

The nucleus would fit across the cell about 5 times.

2 Divide the width of the cell by this number.

30 ÷ 5 = 6 μm ⟵ So the width of the nucleus is approximately 6 μm.

Making Estimates

It's really not far to the end of the section now, so keep going.

Q1 The diagram below shows a mitochondrian measured under an electron microscope. The length of the mitochondrian is given on the diagram. Estimate the width (*x*) of the mitochondrian.

x μm

4.5 μm

.... μm

Q2 A mining company has extracted 29 128 kg of ore from the ground. From this, they are able to produce pure metal with a mass of one fifth of the original ore. Use estimation to calculate the mass of pure metal they can produce from the ore to one significant figure.

.... kg

Q3 A car travels 28 metres every second. Estimate how far it would travel in 11 seconds. Give your answer to one significant figure.

.... m

Q4 Sabrina is investigating the population of dandelions in a park with an area of 3200 m². Using quadrats, she works out that the mean number of dandelions per m² is 9. She multiplies the area by the mean number to get a population of 28 800. Use estimation to check whether Sabrina's answer is correct.

.... dandelions

Calculating Sin x and Sin⁻¹ x

This is a bonus page for all of the Edexcel International GCSE students out there. You're so lucky...

Example

A beam of light travels from air into water. The angle of incidence (i) is 25°.
The angle of refraction (r) is 19°. Calculate the refractive index (n) of water.

Use the following formula: $n = \dfrac{\sin i}{\sin r}$

1 Plug the numbers you know into the formula.

You don't know n — it's what you're trying to calculate.

$n = \dfrac{\sin i}{\sin r} = \dfrac{\sin 25}{\sin 19}$

i is the angle of incidence.

r is the angle of refraction.

See page 72 for more about using formulas.

2 Work it out using a calculator.

$n = \dfrac{\sin 25}{\sin 19} = 1.29809...$

To do this, type in  `sin` `2` `5` `÷` `sin` `1` `9` `=`

3 Round your answer.

Round to the smallest number of significant figures used in the calculation — see page 6.

You need to round to two significant figures.

1.29809... = 1.3

So the refractive index of water is 1.3.

This number is bigger than 5, so round up.

Example

A student has a mystery substance. Its refractive index (n) is 1.4.
Calculate the critical angle (C) for a light beam travelling from the substance into air.

Use the following formula: $\sin C = \dfrac{1}{n}$

1 Plug the numbers you know into the formula.

You don't know C — it's what you're trying to calculate.

$\sin C = \dfrac{1}{n} = \dfrac{1}{1.4}$

n is the refractive index.

2 Do the division.

$\sin C = \dfrac{1}{1.4} = 0.71428...$

Don't do any rounding yet. Wait until the end of the calculation — you've still got to get C on its own.

3 Use a calculator to get C on its own.

$C = \sin^{-1} 0.71428...$
$C = 45.584... = 46°$

To do this, type in  `shift` `sin` and then your previous answer.

So the critical angle is 46°.

Calculating Sin *x* and Sin⁻¹ *x*

Again, these questions are reserved especially for Edexcel International GCSE students. Enjoy.

Q1 A beam of light travels from air into another substance. The angle of incidence is 21° and the angle of refraction is 17°. Calculate the refractive index of the substance.

$$n = \frac{\sin i}{\sin r}$$

....

Q2 A beam of light travels from air into glass with an angle of incidence of 27°. The angle of refraction is 17°. Calculate the refractive index of the glass.

$$n = \frac{\sin i}{\sin r}$$

....

Q3 A student does an experiment to find the refractive index of a substance. The refractive index of the substance is 1.44. Calculate the critical angle for a light beam travelling from the substance into air. Give your answer to two significant figures.

$$\sin C = \frac{1}{n}$$

....°

Q4 A beam of light travels from air into ethanol. The angle of incidence is 31°. The refractive index of ethanol is 1.36. Calculate the angle of refraction. Give your answer to the nearest degree.

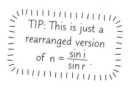

TIP: This is just a rearranged version of $n = \frac{\sin i}{\sin r}$.

$$\sin r = \frac{\sin i}{n}$$

....°

Section 1 — Calculations

Drawing Tables

Once you've collected some data, it's not much use unless it's organised in some way. Tables are a great way of doing this. When you've drawn a table you might then be able to spot patterns you never dreamed of... or at least it will make drawing a chart or graph easier.

Example

Below are the results of three repeats of an experiment in which the volume of gas produced in a reaction was measured at three temperatures, 10 °C, 20 °C and 30 °C. Put this data into a table.

10 °C	20 °C	30 °C		10 °C	20 °C	30 °C		10 °C	20 °C	30 °C
32 cm³	60 cm³	70 cm³		28 cm³	47 cm³	68 cm³		37 cm³	51 cm³	72 cm³

1 **Decide how many rows and columns you need.**

Three temperatures were tested, so you need three rows plus a row or two for the headings.
The experiment was repeated three times, so you need four columns to include one for a heading.

2 **Draw a nice, neat table using a ruler.**

Make sure you make the rows tall enough to write clearly in.

3 **Label each row and column, and put the units in the headings so that you don't have to repeat them throughout the table.**

Put the data in order so that the variable you're changing is getting bigger.

Temperature (°C)	Volume (cm³)		
	Repeat 1	Repeat 2	Repeat 3
10			
20			
30			

Use sensible headings so that it's clear what each column and row is.

4 **Fill in the rest of the table with the data.**

Temperature (°C)	Volume (cm³)		
	Repeat 1	Repeat 2	Repeat 3
10	32	28	37
20	60	47	51
30	70	68	72

There should be a number in every space.

Tables like this often have a final column to show the mean of the repeats. See p.2 for more on calculating means.

Drawing Tables

Now it's your turn. Here's some data from some experiments for you to practise putting into tables.

Q1 Some students were investigating how long a reaction took in seconds at three different temperatures: 10 °C, 20 °C and 30 °C. They repeated the experiment three times. Put their data into a table.

10 °C	20 °C	30 °C
31 s	22 s	10 s
30 s	19 s	11 s
29 s	20 s	11 s

Q2 Milly investigated how effective two antibiotics (A and B) are. She applied each antibiotic to a paper disc and put the discs in a Petri dish of bacteria. After two days she measured the space that had been cleared around each disc. She repeated her experiment three times. Draw a table to display her data.

A	B		A	B		A	B
7 mm	1 mm		6 mm	3 mm		8 mm	2 mm

Q3 Some students are investigating how increasing the surface area of a parachute affects how long it takes to fall from a certain height. They repeat the experiment four times. Put their data below into a table.

25 cm²	36 cm²	49 cm²		25 cm²	36 cm²	49 cm²
4.2 s	6.9 s	9.7 s		4.6 s	5.1 s	9.6 s
25 cm²	36 cm²	49 cm²		25 cm²	36 cm²	49 cm²
4.3 s	7.2 s	9.5 s		4.4 s	7.1 s	9.3 s

Using Frequency Tables

A frequency table is just a table that shows how often something occurs. All you have to do is draw a load of sticks and then count them to give you the frequency. It doesn't get much better than that.

Example

Below are the results of an investigation into the numbers of leaves affected by rose black spot on 20 different rose plants. Put these results into a frequency table.

$$5 \quad 4 \quad 0 \quad 3 \quad 3 \quad 5 \quad 0 \quad 1 \quad 0 \quad 4$$
$$2 \quad 5 \quad 5 \quad 0 \quad 0 \quad 0 \quad 2 \quad 1 \quad 2 \quad 5$$

1 **Decide how many rows you need (you'll need three columns).**
Then draw a neat table and label each row and column.

Frequency tables usually have three columns — one for the values or names of the data, one for the tallies and one for the frequency.

The values range from 0 to 5 so you need six rows, plus one for a heading.

Make sure you put the values in increasing order.

Number of leaves	Tally	Frequency
0		
1		
2		
3		
4		
5		

If the data values are spread over a wide range, you can put them into groups, instead of entering individual values.

2 **Draw a tally mark in the correct row in the tally column to represent each piece of data.**

It can be helpful to cross off the data in the question as you enter it into the table, so that you don't count each piece of data more than once.

Number of leaves	Tally	Frequency
0	ⅢⅠ	
1	Ⅱ	
2	Ⅲ	
3	Ⅱ	
4	Ⅱ	
5	Ⅲ	

When you get to 5 results you write ⅢⅠ, not ⅠⅠⅠⅠⅠ. This makes it easier to keep track of the numbers.

3 **Add up the tally marks in each row to find the frequency for each value.**

Number of leaves	Tally	Frequency
0	ⅢⅠ	6
1	Ⅱ	2
2	Ⅲ	3
3	Ⅱ	2
4	Ⅱ	2
5	Ⅲ	5

The frequency values should add up to the total number of pieces of data.

Using Frequency Tables

Grab some sticks (or maybe just a ruler) — it's time to draw some frequency tables.

Q1 Some students were investigating the maximum heart rate of a group of runners. They asked each runner to run 400 m as fast as they could and recorded their maximum heart rate. Complete the frequency table below.

| 180 | 176 | 170 | 184 | 162 | 181 | 177 | 166 | 169 | 180 |
| 175 | 160 | 182 | 173 | 177 | 176 | 168 | 183 | 178 | 175 |

Heart rate	Tally	Frequency
160 - 164		
165 - 169		
170 - 174		
175 - 179		
180 - 184		

TIP: the table contains groups of values so the tally just needs to go in the right group.

Q2 A student tested the pH of some household substances. Put their data below into a frequency table.

| 7 | 3 | 8 | 9 | 6 | 8 | 3 | 11 | 8 | 4 |
| 8 | 8 | 9 | 11 | 3 | 5 | 10 | 8 | 3 | 3 |

Drawing Bar Charts

It's not too tricky to turn a table of data into a bar chart. You just need to draw the axes, work out how tall the bars need to be, and then you can get your colouring pencils out to finish the job. Nothing more to it.

Example

A student has recorded the mass of carbohydrate, protein and fat in two different foods. Draw a bar chart to show this data.

Food Group	Food A (g)	Food B (g)
Carbohydrate	18	22
Protein	29	17
Fat	6	12

This is categorical data — there are three distinct categories within the data, which makes it ideal for drawing a bar chart. You can also use bar charts to show discrete data (data that only takes certain values, where there's no in-between value, e.g. number of people).

1 **Work out which variable needs to go on each axis, and whether you need a key.**

The categories go on the x-axis — the one along the bottom.
The dependent variable (the thing that was measured for each category) goes on the y-axis — the one up the side.
If there's more than one set of data for each category, you'll need to use a key.

These are the categories.

Food Group	Food A (g)	Food B (g)
Carbohydrate	18	22
Protein	29	17
Fat	6	12

The mass of nutrient is the dependent variable — it's what was measured.

Here there are two sets of data for each category.

2 **Choose a sensible scale for your axes and label them. You also need to make the x-axis long enough to leave a space between each category. The axes should fill at least half of the space that you're given.**

Make sure you include a label and the units (if there are any) for each axis.

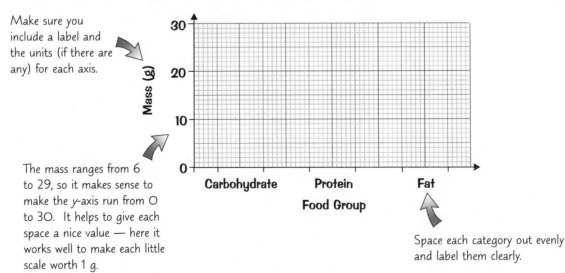

The mass ranges from 6 to 29, so it makes sense to make the y-axis run from 0 to 30. It helps to give each space a nice value — here it works well to make each little scale worth 1 g.

Space each category out evenly and label them clearly.

3 Draw the bars neatly with a sharp pencil. Make sure each bar is the same width.

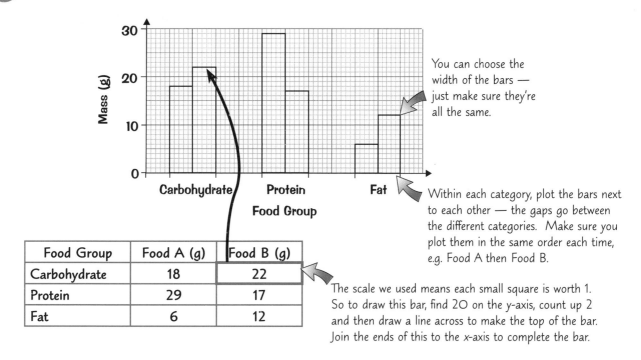

You can choose the width of the bars — just make sure they're all the same.

Within each category, plot the bars next to each other — the gaps go between the different categories. Make sure you plot them in the same order each time, e.g. Food A then Food B.

Food Group	Food A (g)	Food B (g)
Carbohydrate	18	22
Protein	29	17
Fat	6	12

The scale we used means each small square is worth 1. So to draw this bar, find 20 on the y-axis, count up 2 and then draw a line across to make the top of the bar. Join the ends of this to the x-axis to complete the bar.

4 If you have more than one set of data then shade the bars of each set differently and draw a key.

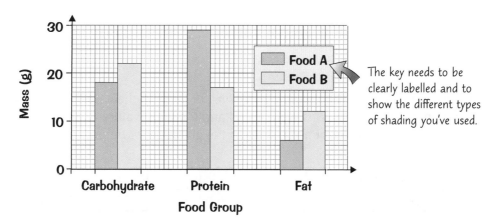

The key needs to be clearly labelled and to show the different types of shading you've used.

5 Shading in bars on a graph isn't as much fun as shading in cows...

Section 2 — Presenting Data

Drawing Bar Charts

It's time for you to turn some data tables into pretty bar charts. Sharpen your pencil and grab a ruler...

Q1 Chris carried out an experiment to find the energy content of four food samples. His results are in the table below. Draw a bar chart of his results on the graph paper.

Food Sample	A	B	C	D
Energy (J/g)	29	11	37	16

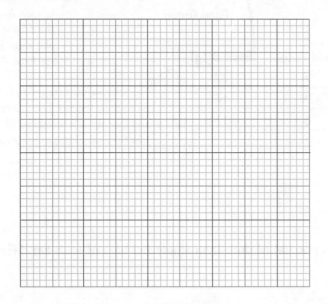

Q2 Gemma was investigating exothermic reactions for use in a 'heat pack'. Five different chemical reactions were tested and the temperature rise was recorded. Draw a bar chart of her results on the graph paper below.

Reaction	1	2	3	4	5
Temperature rise (°C)	10	21	53	17	26

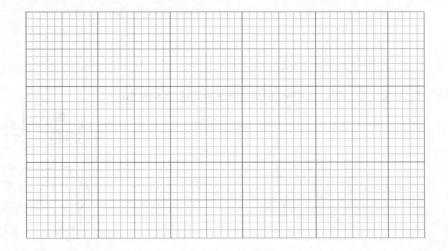

Q3 Liz carried out a survey on two year groups to find out students' masses. She then calculated the average mass for males and females in each year. Draw a bar chart of her results below on the graph paper.

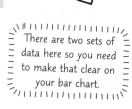
There are two sets of data here so you need to make that clear on your bar chart.

	Average Mass (kg)	
Year	Male	Female
10	54	51
11	57	53

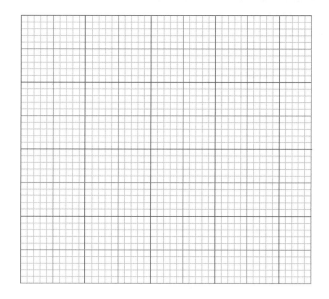

Q4 Some students were investigating the time taken for different balls to roll down two different ramps. They calculated the average time taken for each ball. Draw a bar chart of the results on the graph paper below.

	Average time (s)		
Ramp	Ping pong ball	Golf ball	Tennis ball
A	2.4	1.9	2.1
B	3.2	2.5	2.8

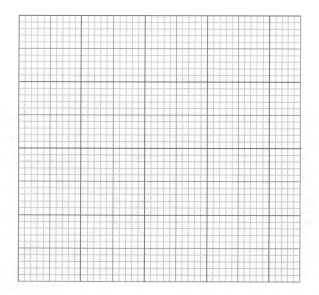

Section 2 — Presenting Data

Drawing Histograms

Histograms may look like innocent bar charts, but don't be fooled — they've got a few hidden depths.
Luckily you've got these nice steps to follow and before you know it you'll be drawing them in your sleep.

Example

Ali was investigating the length of beetles in her garden.
Her results are shown in the table below.
Draw a histogram of her results.

Length (mm)	Frequency
0 < x ≤ 10	32
10 < x ≤ 15	36
15 < x ≤ 18	24
18 < x ≤ 22	28
22 < x ≤ 30	16

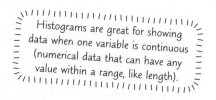

Histograms are great for showing data when one variable is continuous (numerical data that can have any value within a range, like length).

< just means 'less than' and ≤ means 'less than or equal to'. > means 'greater than' and ≥ means 'greater than or equal to'.

1 Work out the class width of each class by subtracting the smallest number in each class from the largest number.

It's this column of numbers that's used to work out the class widths.

Length (mm)	Frequency	Class Width
0 < x ≤ 10	32	10 − 0 = 10
10 < x ≤ 15	36	15 − 10 = 5
15 < x ≤ 18	24	18 − 15 = 3
18 < x ≤ 22	28	22 − 18 = 4
22 < x ≤ 30	16	30 − 22 = 8

It's useful to add another column to do this working in.

Each of these groups of lengths is known as a class.

2 Divide the frequency of each class by the class width to work out frequency density.

Length (mm)	Frequency	Class Width	Frequency Density
0 < x ≤ 10	32	10 − 0 = 10	32 ÷ 10 = 3.2
10 < x ≤ 15	36	15 − 10 = 5	36 ÷ 5 = 7.2
15 < x ≤ 18	24	18 − 15 = 3	24 ÷ 3 = 8
18 < x ≤ 22	28	22 − 18 = 4	28 ÷ 4 = 7
22 < x ≤ 30	16	30 − 22 = 8	16 ÷ 8 = 2

Again, adding another column to work out the frequency density is a good idea. You're less likely to make a mistake if you write out your working.

Frequency   Class width

3 Draw your axes with a sensible scale and label them. The axes should take up at least half of the space on the graph paper you've been given. Always draw frequency density on the *y*-axis and the classes on the *x*-axis.

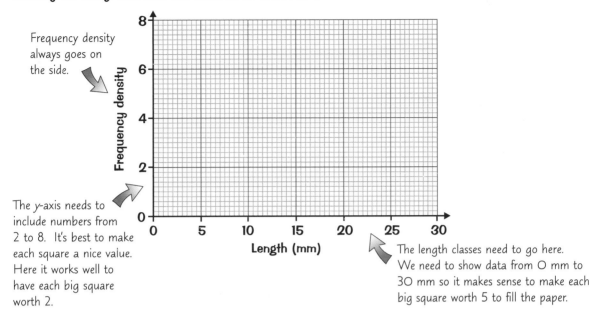

Frequency density always goes on the side.

The *y*-axis needs to include numbers from 2 to 8. It's best to make each square a nice value. Here it works well to have each big square worth 2.

The length classes need to go here. We need to show data from 0 mm to 30 mm so it makes sense to make each big square worth 5 to fill the paper.

4 Draw the bars neatly with a sharp pencil. Each bar needs to be as wide as the class it is representing.

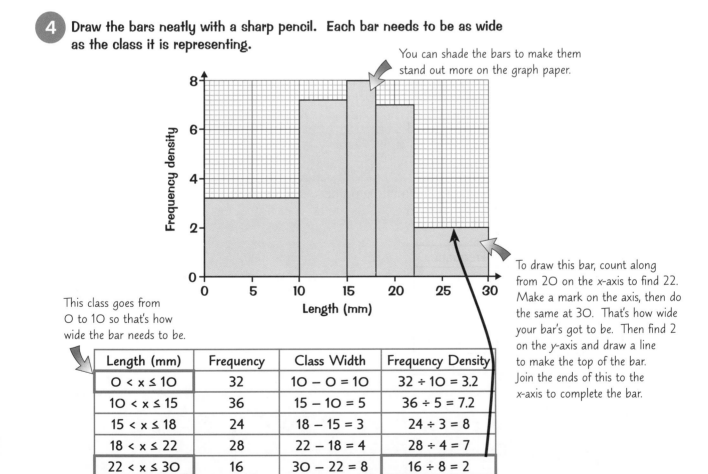

You can shade the bars to make them stand out more on the graph paper.

This class goes from 0 to 10 so that's how wide the bar needs to be.

To draw this bar, count along from 20 on the *x*-axis to find 22. Make a mark on the axis, then do the same at 30. That's how wide your bar's got to be. Then find 2 on the *y*-axis and draw a line to make the top of the bar. Join the ends of this to the *x*-axis to complete the bar.

Length (mm)	Frequency	Class Width	Frequency Density
0 < x ≤ 10	32	10 − 0 = 10	32 ÷ 10 = 3.2
10 < x ≤ 15	36	15 − 10 = 5	36 ÷ 5 = 7.2
15 < x ≤ 18	24	18 − 15 = 3	24 ÷ 3 = 8
18 < x ≤ 22	28	22 − 18 = 4	28 ÷ 4 = 7
22 < x ≤ 30	16	30 − 22 = 8	16 ÷ 8 = 2

Section 2 — Presenting Data

Drawing Histograms

Grab a ruler and a calculator and get stuck into these questions. You might just learn to love histograms...

Q1 Some students were investigating the height of apple trees in an orchard. Draw a histogram of their results below.

Height (m)	Frequency
$0 < x \leq 2$	38
$2 < x \leq 3.5$	30
$3.5 < x \leq 4$	22
$4 < x \leq 4.5$	18
$4.5 < x \leq 6$	15

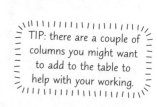

TIP: there are a couple of columns you might want to add to the table to help with your working.

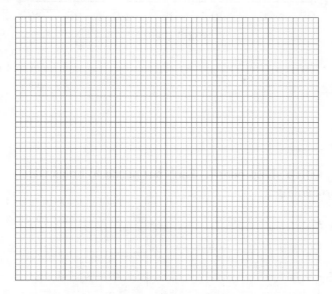

Q2 Some students are investigating the melting points of different substances. Draw a histogram of the results below.

Melting Point (°C)	Frequency
$0 < x \leq 15$	6
$15 < x \leq 30$	9
$30 < x \leq 40$	13
$40 < x \leq 50$	11
$50 < x \leq 70$	16

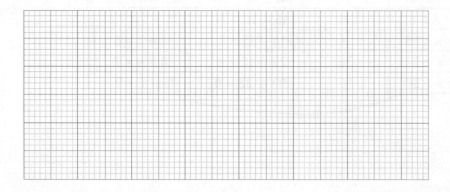

Section 2 — Presenting Data

Q3   Draw a histogram of the data below.   CHEMISTRY

Concentration (g/dm³)	Frequency
$0 < x \le 0.4$	2
$0.4 < x \le 1.0$	9
$1.0 < x \le 1.2$	10
$1.2 < x \le 1.6$	16
$1.6 < x \le 2.4$	4

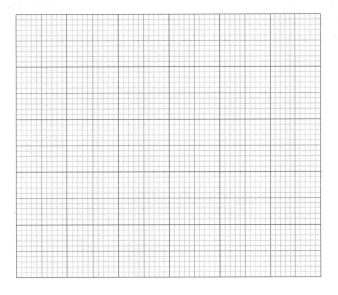

Q4   Ellie did an investigation into body temperature.   BIOLOGY
Draw a histogram of her results below.

Body Temperature (°C)	Frequency
$35.5 < x \le 36.5$	5
$36.5 < x \le 36.75$	2
$36.75 < x \le 37.25$	5
$37.25 < x \le 37.5$	1
$37.5 < x \le 38.5$	1

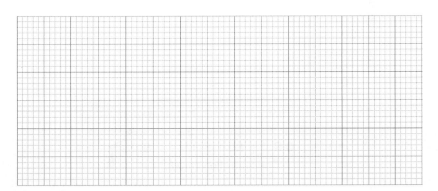

Section 2 — Presenting Data

Drawing Scatter Diagrams

Raw data isn't much fun to look at. It's much nicer to gaze lovingly at a graph. Scatter diagrams are graphs where you plot the points and then draw a line of best fit. They're great at showing how two variables relate to each other — so both of your variables need to be numbers.

Example

Sophie was investigating the effect of concentration on the rate of a reaction. She tested four different concentrations and timed how long it took to produce 20 cm³ of gas in each reaction. Her results are in the table below. Plot her data on a scatter diagram.

Concentration (mol/dm³)	0.5	1.0	1.5	2.0
Time taken (s)	38	19	21	9

1 Decide which variable is going on each axis.

The independent variable (the thing that was changed) goes on the *x*-axis (across the bottom).
The dependent variable (the thing that was measured) goes on the *y*-axis (up the side).

Concentration (mol/dm³)	0.5	1.0	1.5	2.0
Time taken (s)	38	19	21	9

◁ This is the variable that was changed.

◁ This is the variable that was measured.

2 Draw your axes and label them. The axes should sensibly fill the space you're given and you should make each square of graph paper worth a nice value so it's easy to plot.

The time ranges from 9 to 38, so it makes sense to make the *y*-axis run from 0 to 40. The graph paper is 4 big squares tall, so if we start at 0 and make each large square worth 10 it will take 4 squares to get to 40. Nice.

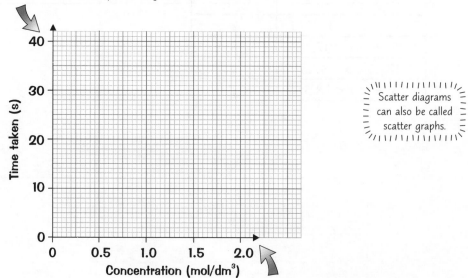

Scatter diagrams can also be called scatter graphs.

Concentration goes on the bottom and the data range is 0.5 to 2.0. The graph paper is 5 big squares wide. So 4 squares each worth 0.5 seems a sensible scale.

3 Plot the points using a sharp pencil and make neat little crosses (<u>not</u> blobs).

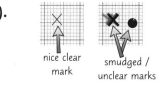

nice clear mark

smudged / unclear marks

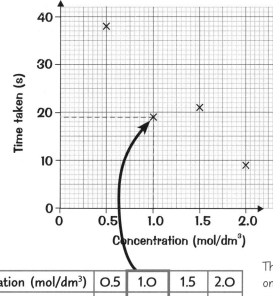

Concentration (mol/dm³)	0.5	1.0	1.5	2.0
Time taken (s)	38	19	21	9

The scale we used means each small square on the y-axis is worth 1. So to plot this point go across to 1.0 on the x-axis and then count up 9 squares from 10 on the y-axis to get 19, and put a neat cross there.

4 Then draw a line of best fit — a line that passes through, or as near as possible to, as many of the points as you can. These help to show any trends in the data. Ignore anomalous results when drawing them.

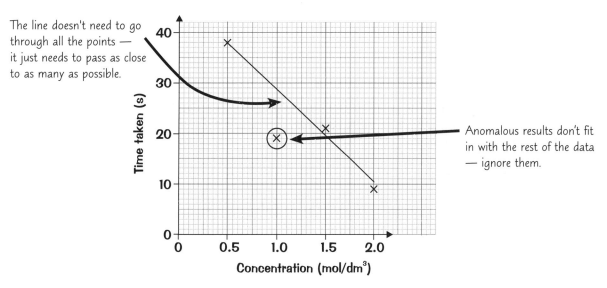

The line doesn't need to go through all the points — it just needs to pass as close to as many as possible.

Anomalous results don't fit in with the rest of the data — ignore them.

5 Sometimes your points will follow a curved pattern and so you'll need to draw a curved line of best fit.

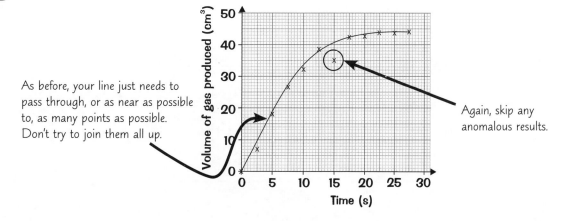

As before, your line just needs to pass through, or as near as possible to, as many points as possible. Don't try to join them all up.

Again, skip any anomalous results.

Drawing Scatter Diagrams

Right, your turn. Here's some data from experiments for you to practise plotting on a scatter diagram.

Q1 Ash carried out an experiment to investigate how temperature affects the rate of a reaction. Plot a scatter diagram of his results on the graph paper below. Draw a line of best fit.

Temperature (°C)	0	5	10	15	20	25	30
Rate of Reaction (cm³/s)	0	3	7	8	17	16	19

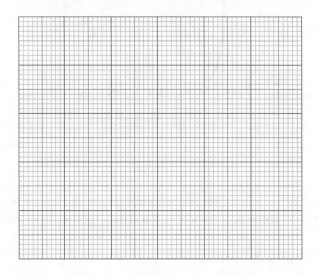

Q2 Lara was investigating the relationship between current and voltage. Plot a scatter diagram of her results on the graph paper below. Include a line of best fit.

Current (A)	2	3	4	5	6	7	8	9	10
Voltage (V)	1.9	3.2	3.8	5.0	5.8	7.2	7.8	8.4	9.8

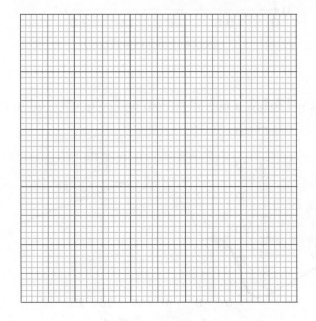

Section 2 — Presenting Data

Q3 Sarita was investigating the relationship between temperature and rate of reaction. She used a chemical reaction where the contents of the beaker became cloudy over time. She measured the rate of reaction by timing how long it took for a mark under the beaker to disappear from view. Plot a scatter diagram of her results below and draw a line of best fit.

Temperature (°C)	10	20	30	40	50
Time taken for mark to disappear (s)	195	150	110	85	50

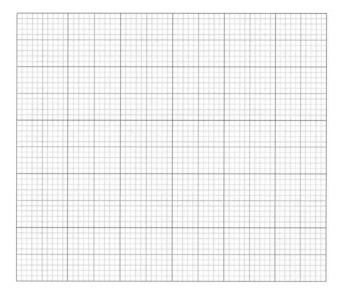

Q4 Some students were investigating the effect of light intensity on the rate of photosynthesis of pondweed in a beaker of water. The light intensity was varied by placing a lamp at different distances from the plant. The rate of photosynthesis was measured by counting how many bubbles of gas were produced in one minute. Plot a scatter diagram of the results below and draw a line of best fit.

Distance (cm)	0	5	10	15	20	25	30	35	40	45	50
Bubbles per minute	245	210	185	155	120	90	65	50	40	25	20

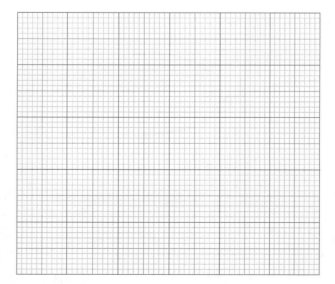

Uncertainties

Everyone is uncertain sometimes and measurements are too. In this case, the uncertainty is the amount of error that the measurements might have. This can come from random errors or from limits in the equipment you use to do the measuring. Not only can you calculate the uncertainty but you can plot it on a graph too. So all the world can see how uncertain your measurements are. Fantastic.

Example

Miles carried out a respiration experiment. He measured the volume of carbon dioxide produced at different temperatures. He repeated his experiment three times. Some of his results are shown in the table below. Calculate the uncertainty of the mean and plot this as a range bar on the graph below.

Temperature (°C)	Volume of CO_2 (cm^3)			
	Repeat 1	Repeat 2	Repeat 3	Mean
10	1.3	1.7	1.9	1.6

1 Work out the range of the results by subtracting the smallest number from the largest number.

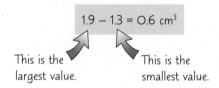

$$1.9 - 1.3 = 0.6 \text{ cm}^3$$

This is the largest value.

This is the smallest value.

2 Divide the range by 2 to find the uncertainty of the mean.

$$0.6 \div 2 = 0.3 \text{ cm}^3$$

So the uncertainty of the mean is: $1.6 \pm 0.3 \text{ cm}^3$

This sign stands for 'plus or minus' — it means the actual value of the mean could be anywhere between 1.6 + 0.3 (1.9) and 1.6 − 0.3 (1.3).

3 Use this uncertainty to plot a range bar.

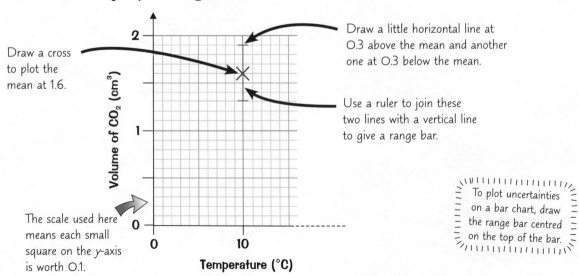

Draw a cross to plot the mean at 1.6.

Draw a little horizontal line at 0.3 above the mean and another one at 0.3 below the mean.

Use a ruler to join these two lines with a vertical line to give a range bar.

The scale used here means each small square on the *y*-axis is worth 0.1.

To plot uncertainties on a bar chart, draw the range bar centred on the top of the bar.

Uncertainties

Now it's time to practise working out those uncertainties. Calculators at the ready.

Q1 Some students carried out an investigation into the speed of a trolley travelling down two different ramps. Calculate the uncertainties of the means and plot these as range bars on the bar chart below.

	Speed (cm/s)			
Ramp	Repeat 1	Repeat 2	Repeat 3	Mean
A	46	42	44	44
B	30	24	27	27

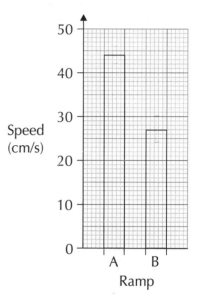

Uncertainty of the mean for:

Ramp A = ... cm/s

Ramp B = ... cm/s

Q2 A student carried out an experiment to investigate how concentration affects the temperature change during a reaction. Calculate the uncertainties of the means. Plot the uncertainties as range bars on the scatter diagram below.

	Temperature change (°C)			
Concentration (g/dm³)	Repeat 1	Repeat 2	Repeat 3	Mean
10	9	11	13	11
20	15	17	16	16
30	17	23	20	20

Uncertainty of the mean at:

10 g/dm³ = ... °C

20 g/dm³ = ... °C

30 g/dm³ = ... °C

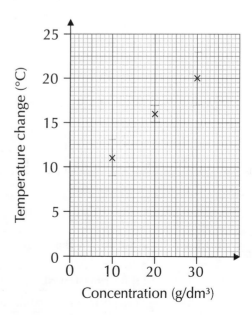

Reading Tables

When data is laid out nicely in a table, it makes it easier to find the information you want to know. You'd be searching through the raw data for ages otherwise. Figuring out tables is easy when you know how...

Example

Three groups of plants were treated with different fertilisers and left to grow for three weeks. Which fertiliser was the most effective?

Fertiliser	A	B	C
Mean Growth (mm)	13.5	19.5	5.5

1 Find the row or column that contains the measurements you're looking for.

Fertiliser	A	B	C
Mean Growth (mm)	13.5	19.5	5.5

The question asks you to compare plant growth, so this is the row you'll need to look at.

2 Pick out the piece of information the question is asking for.

Fertiliser	A	B	C
Mean Growth (mm)	13.5	19.5	5.5

You're looking for the largest number in the row, which is 19.5 mm — so fertiliser B was the most effective.

Example

Derek did a survey to find out how much exercise his classmates did in a week. His results are in the table below. How many students did less than 2 hours of exercise during the week?

Time (mins)	0 - 59	60 - 119	120 - 179	180 +
Number of students	11	16	9	13

1 Find the row or column that contains the measurements you're looking for.

Time (mins)	0 - 59	60 - 119	120 - 179	180 +
Number of students	11	16	9	13

The question asks you to look at the time the students spent exercising, so this is the row you need to look at first.

2 Pick out the pieces of information the question is asking for.

Time (mins)	0 - 59	60 - 119	120 - 179	180 +
Number of students	11	16	9	13

You're only interested in the students who did less than 2 hours of exercise, so that's the first two columns.

3 Add them together to get the total.

Time (mins)	0 - 59	60 - 119
Number of students	11	16

Total = 11 + 16 = 27 students

Reading Tables

Aaaaand now it's your turn. Here are some tables full of data, just waiting to be read...

Q1 Three catalysts were tested for their effectiveness in a particular chemical reaction. The results are in the table.

Catalyst	Rate of Reaction (cm³/s)
A	17.5
B	10.5
C	4.5

a) Which catalyst gave the highest rate of reaction?

....

b) What was the difference between the highest rate of reaction and the lowest rate of reaction?

.... cm³/s

Q2 The table shows some information about different energy sources used to generate electricity.

If a table has loads of data, just work out what information the question wants — ignore the rest.

	Coal	Gas	Nuclear	Wind
Efficiency	36%	50%	38%	35%
Energy output per year (millions of units)	8000	5000	7000	150
CO_2 emissions per unit (g)	920	440	110	none
Average cost of energy per unit (p)	2.5	2	5	3

a) Which energy source has the highest energy output per year?

....

b) What is the difference in CO_2 emissions per unit between coal and gas energy?

.... g

Q3 Two crops were grown in different fields and their yield was recorded each year.

Yield (tonnes)	Crop A	Crop B
Year 1	7.5	6.5
Year 2	6.5	6.0
Year 3	8.0	5.0

a) What was the total yield of crop A over the first three years?

.... tonnes

b) What was the total crop yield in the third year?

.... tonnes

Section 3 — Analysing Data

Using Pie Charts

Pie charts are divided into sectors that represent categories — the size of each sector tells you how much of the total data is in that category. Think of data like a hot apple filling. Mmmm...

Example

Gemma investigated the nutritional content of a type of food. The pie chart shows the percentage of each substance that makes up the food.

Calculate the percentage content of protein in the food.

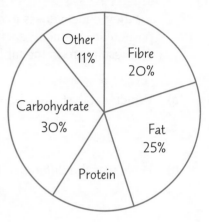

1 Add up the percentages that are given in the pie chart.

20% + 25% + 30% + 11% = 86% ⟵ So fibre, fat, carbohydrate and 'other' make up 86% of the food.

2 Subtract the total percentage from 100%.

100% − 86% = 14% ⟵ So protein makes up 14% of the food.

Example

Gemma is still investigating the nutritional content of the same type of food. Her sample has a mass of 80 g.

Calculate the mass of carbohydrate in her sample.

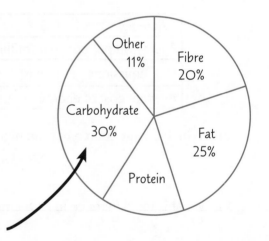

1 Find the sector you want and read off the value.

You can read this straight off the pie chart.
Find the sector for carbohydrate and read off the percentage — 30%.

2 Turn the percentage into a decimal.

Divide the percentage by 100. ⟹ 30 ÷ 100 = 0.3

3 Multiply the decimal by the total given in the question.

0.3 × 80 g = 24 g ⟵ So there are 24 g of carbohydrate in the sample.

The total mass of the sample is 80 g.

4 Enough about pies. Try running like a slug.

Using Pie Charts

All it takes is some practice, then getting data from a pie chart will be as easy as... well, pie.

Q1 The pie chart below shows the relative amounts of ionising radiation from different sources that residents are exposed to in one town. What percentage of the radiation comes from the nuclear industry?

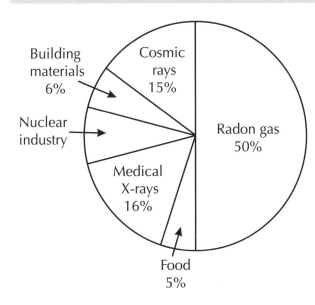

.... %

Q2 Over one month, a doctor's surgery recorded the type of pathogen that patients with communicable diseases were infected with. The pie chart shows the results.

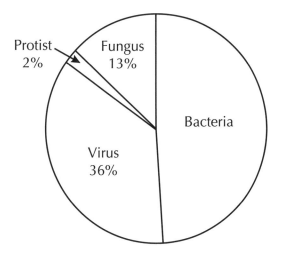

a) What percentage of patients were infected with a bacterial disease?

.... %

b) Over the month, 900 patients visited the surgery with a communicable disease. How many of the patients had a disease caused by a virus?

.... patients

Section 3 — Analysing Data

Interpreting Bar Charts

Bar charts are really useful for comparing data, and they're really pretty too... (Well, I think so).

Example

A student was comparing how much energy four different activities use. The results are shown in this bar chart.

How much energy per minute does swimming use up?

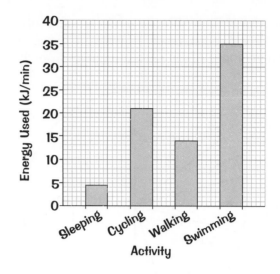

① Pick the bar you need to look at.

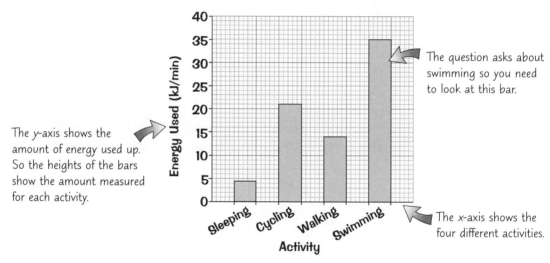

The question asks about swimming so you need to look at this bar.

The y-axis shows the amount of energy used up. So the heights of the bars show the amount measured for each activity.

The x-axis shows the four different activities.

② Read across from the height of the bar to the value on the y-axis.

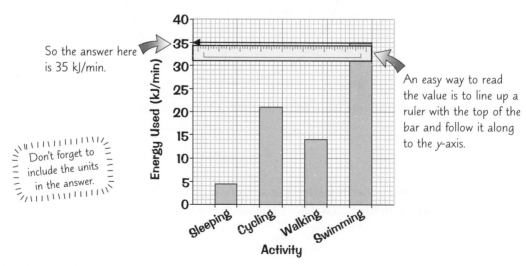

So the answer here is 35 kJ/min.

An easy way to read the value is to line up a ruler with the top of the bar and follow it along to the y-axis.

Don't forget to include the units in the answer.

③ Time to limbo.

Section 3 — Analysing Data

Example

The percentages of dark- and light-coloured moths in two different towns are shown in the bar chart opposite.

What is the difference between the percentages of dark-coloured moths in town A and town B?

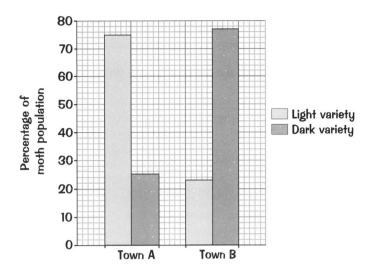

1 **Pick the bars you need to look at.**

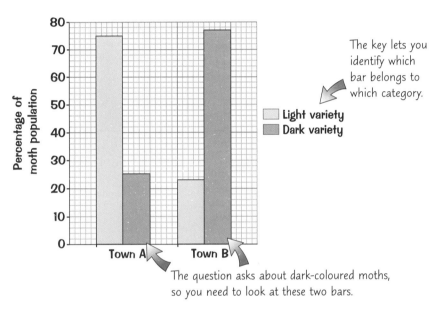

The key lets you identify which bar belongs to which category.

The question asks about dark-coloured moths, so you need to look at these two bars.

2 **Read the values from the *y*-axis.**

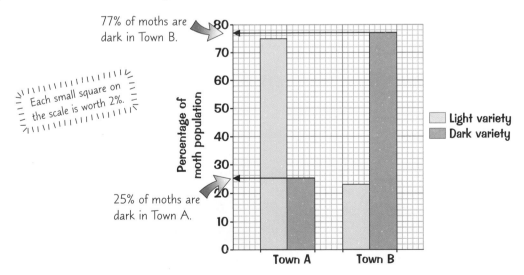

77% of moths are dark in Town B.

Each small square on the scale is worth 2%.

25% of moths are dark in Town A.

3 **Subtract the smaller value from the bigger one to find the difference.**

77% − 25% = 52%

Interpreting Bar Charts

Right, your turn. Grab a ruler and have a go at getting the info out of these bar charts.

Q1   Julie did an experiment to compare the energy content of four fuel samples. Her results are shown in the graph below. Which fuel sample had the highest energy content?

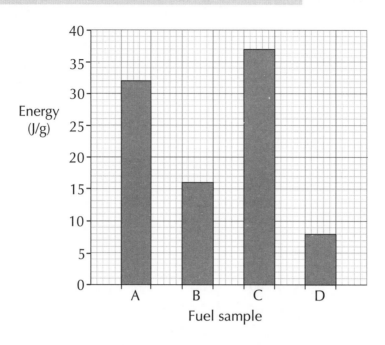

....

Q2   The fat content of butter and olive oil were investigated and the results displayed in a graph. How much more saturated fat does butter contain compared to olive oil?

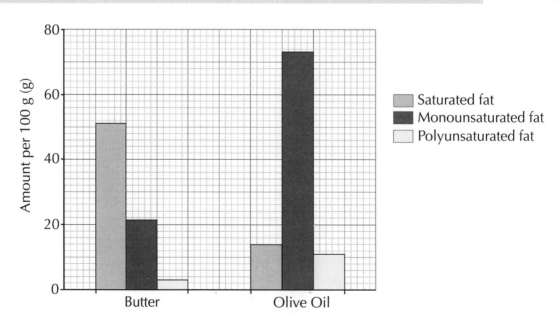

.... g per 100g

Section 3 — Analysing Data

Q3 Yvonne carried out an experiment to compare the amounts of water and decomposing material in two different soil samples. She heated the samples twice — once at 105 °C and again at 550 °C. How much more mass did sample A lose after the two heating stages than sample B?

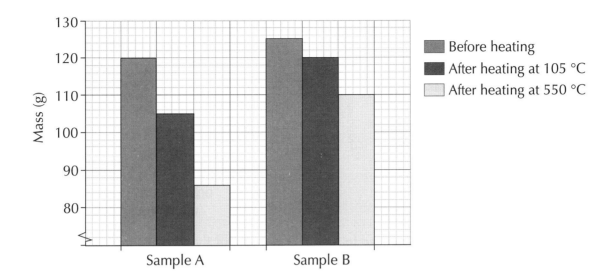

.... g

Q4 Josh is plotting a bar graph of the energy sources a country uses to generate electricity. What percentage should his bar for 'nuclear' be worth?

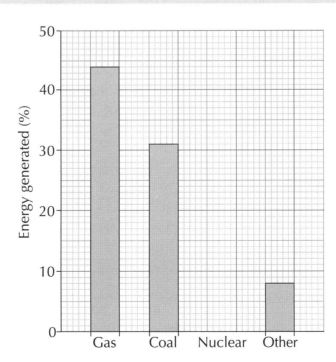

.... %

Section 3 — Analysing Data

Interpreting Histograms

Histograms are kind of like bar charts, but it's the area of the bar that's important rather than the height. That means a bit of calculating is involved to wrestle the data out of them. Calculator at the ready...

Example

Martin was investigating the boiling points of a range of substances. His results are in this histogram.

How many substances had a boiling point between 100 °C and 110 °C?

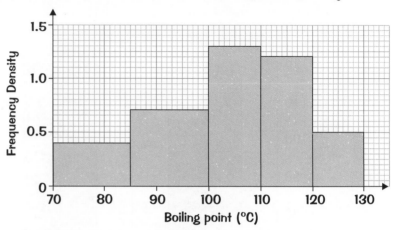

1 Pick the class (or classes) you need to look at and work out the width of the bar.

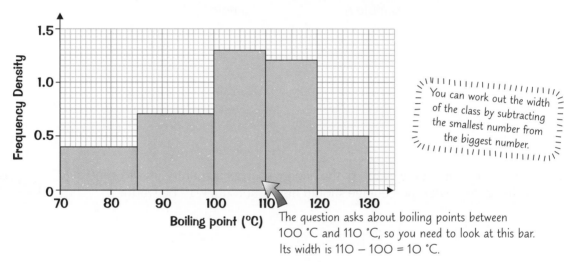

You can work out the width of the class by subtracting the smallest number from the biggest number.

The question asks about boiling points between 100 °C and 110 °C, so you need to look at this bar. Its width is 110 − 100 = 10 °C.

2 Read across from the height of the bar to the number on the *y*-axis.

There are 10 small squares between 1.0 and 1.5, so each square must stand for 0.05. Reading across, the top of the bar is at 1.3.

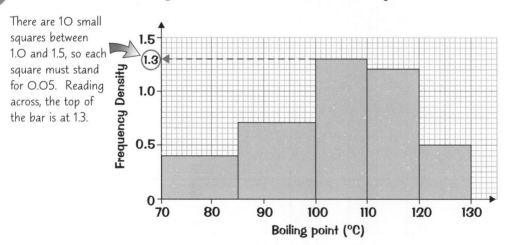

3 Multiply the width of the bar (the class width) by the height of the bar (the frequency density).

10 × 1.3 = 13

Class width

Frequency density

Frequency — this is the number of substances in this class. So 13 substances had a boiling point between 100 and 110 °C.

Interpreting Histograms

It's time to let these histograms know who's boss. Grab your calculator and have a go at these questions...

Q1 A selection of metal items were tested as resistors in an electric circuit. A histogram of their resistances is shown below. How many of the items tested had resistance between 5 Ω and 10 Ω?

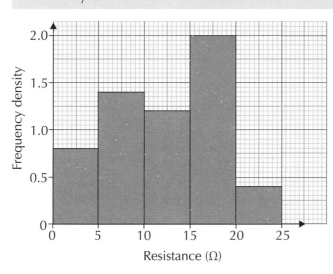

.... items

Q2 Emil was investigating the range of heights of students in his class. He made a histogram of his results. How many students are less than 150 cm tall?

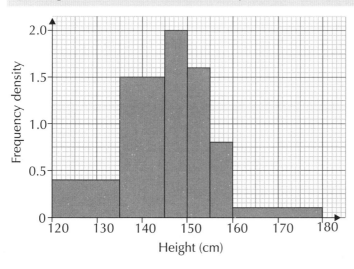

TIP: Work out the frequency for each class separately, then add them together to get the total number of students.

.... students

Q3 The histogram below shows the energy output for different samples of fuel. How many samples have an energy output of more than 20 J/g?

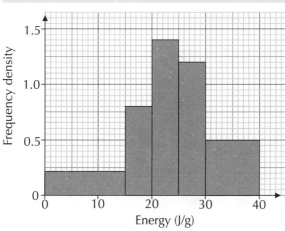

.... samples

Section 3 — Analysing Data

Understanding Correlation

Scatter diagrams are really good at showing the relationship between two variables. And the fun doesn't stop there — you can even describe that relationship with fancy words like positive correlation and negative correlation. I bet you can't wait to get stuck in — it's a page of graphical treats.

Simon did an experiment to investigate how temperature affects the rate of a reaction, and plotted a graph of his results. What type of correlation does the graph show?

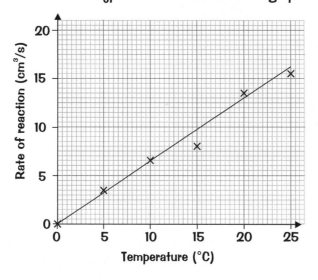

A correlation is a relationship between two variables.

1 Look at the direction of the line of best fit.
There are two types of correlation it could look like (or if you couldn't draw a line of best fit, there's probably no correlation at all).

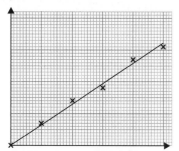

If both values increase together, it's known as a positive correlation.

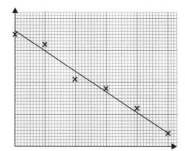

It's called a negative correlation if one value increases as the other decreases.

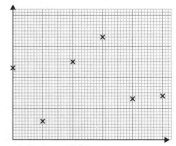

If one variable has no effect on the other, there's no correlation at all. There's no hope of drawing a line of best fit here.

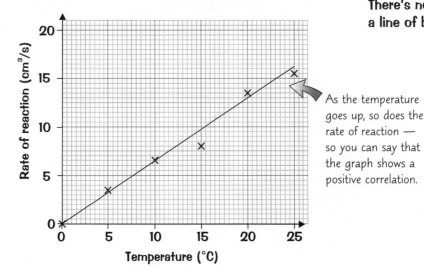

As the temperature goes up, so does the rate of reaction — so you can say that the graph shows a positive correlation.

Understanding Correlation

The ups and downs of relationships — it's exciting stuff. Here are some lovely scatter diagrams complete with lines of best fit so you can put your new-found relationship knowledge to the test.

Q1 Some students did an experiment to find out how increasing the concentration of acid affects the amount of heat produced in a neutralisation reaction. Describe the trend in their results.

A relationship might also be referred to as a trend.

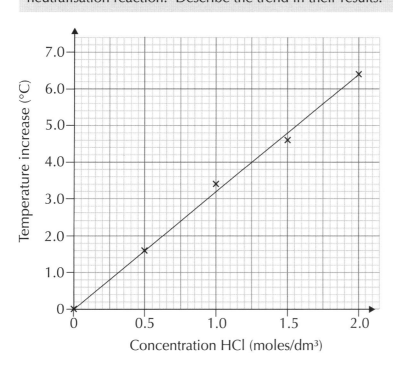

Concentration HCl (moles/dm³)

....
....
....
....
....
....
....
....
....

Q2 The graph below shows the results of a study investigating the link between the number of bees in an area and the temperature of the area. Describe the relationship it shows.

Average temperature (°C)

....
....
....
....
....
....
....
....

Section 3 — Analysing Data

Understanding Proportion

You can take correlation one step further and describe whether the relationship is proportional or not.

Example

The graph on the right shows a positive correlation between temperature and rate of reaction.

Is the relationship proportional?

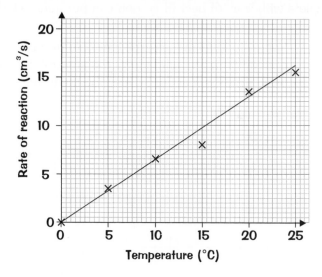

1 Look to see whether both variables increase (or decrease) at the same rate.
There are two types of proportional relationship you could look out for:

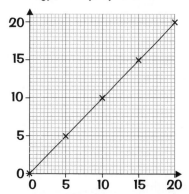

Both values increase at the same rate (e.g. as one thing doubles, the other thing also doubles) — this is a directly proportional relationship.
A trick to spotting these is if the graph is a straight line that passes through the origin (0,0).

This can be written as $x \propto y$ The $\propto$ symbol means 'proportional to'.

As one value increases, the other decreases at the same rate (e.g. as one thing doubles, the other thing halves) — this is an indirectly proportional (or inversely proportional) relationship.

This can be written as $x \propto \frac{1}{y}$

Back to the graph in the question now...

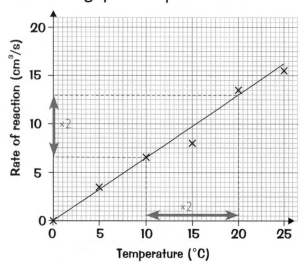

Choose two temperatures, one which is double the other, e.g. 10 °C and 20 °C. Look at what the rate of reaction is at these two temperatures.

At 10 °C, the rate is 6.5 cm³/s
At 20 °C, the rate is 13 cm³/s.

13 ÷ 6.5 = 2, so the rate is doubled as well.

So you can say that the rate of reaction is directly proportional to the temperature.

Or... rate of reaction $\propto$ temperature.

Not all lines of best fit show a proportional relationship — e.g. one variable might double whilst the other triples. They have to change at the same rate for it to be proportional.

Understanding Proportion

In case you haven't quite had enough of relationships, here's one more page of questions. You're welcome.

Q1 A gas syringe was filled with increasing volumes of a gas at a constant temperature. The pressure inside the syringe was measured. Name the type of proportionality the graph shows.

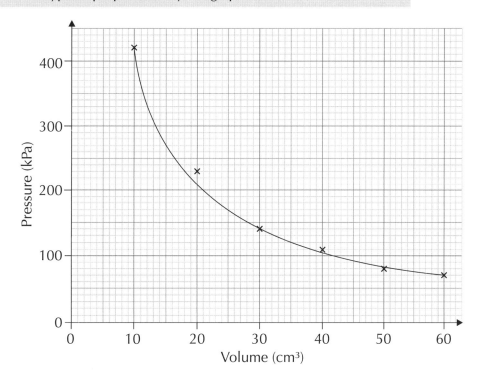

....

Q2 Pratima investigated the effect of different voltages on the current in a circuit. Her results are shown below. Name the type of proportionality the graph shows.

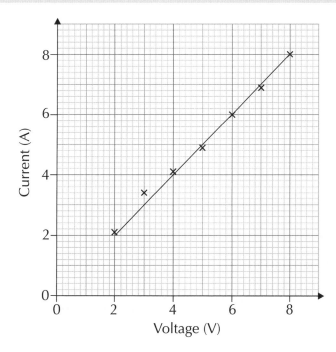

....

Section 3 — Analysing Data

Percentiles

Percentiles show what percentage of a set of data will have a particular value. So, the 20th percentile means that 20% of the data has a value that's equal to, or below, the value of the 20th percentile.

Example

The chart on the right is a percentile growth chart for boys aged between 0 and 1 year.

a) A 6-month-old baby weighs 8 kg. What percentile is the baby in?

b) In a sample of 500 6-month-old babies, how many would weigh 8 kg or less?

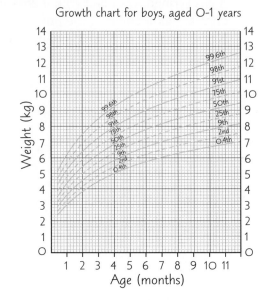

Growth chart for boys, aged 0-1 years

First, focus on part a)...

1 Draw a line up from the x-axis and across from the y-axis using the values in the question. Read off which percentile this data falls within.

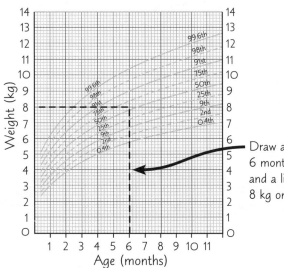

Draw a line up from 6 months on the x-axis and a line across from 8 kg on the y-axis.

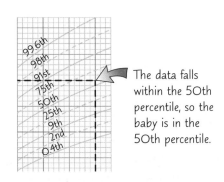

The data falls within the 50th percentile, so the baby is in the 50th percentile.

Now for part b)...

1 Convert the percentile into a decimal.

Six-month-old babies that weigh 8 kg are in the 50th percentile.
This means that 50% of six-month-old babies will weigh 8 kg or less.

50 ÷ 100 = 0.5 — Convert 50% to a decimal by dividing by 100.

See page 14 if you need a reminder about percentages.

2 Multiply the decimal by the sample size.

Use the decimal to work out 50% of 500. → 0.5 × 500 = 250 ← So 250 6-month-old babies would weigh 8 kg or less.

3 Give a goldfish a present.

Percentiles

This page of questions combines your knowledge of reading from graphs with your knowledge of percentages. All of that learning has got to be used somewhere, so what better place than here...

Q1 The chart below is a percentile growth chart for boys aged from 0 to 1 year. **BIOLOGY**

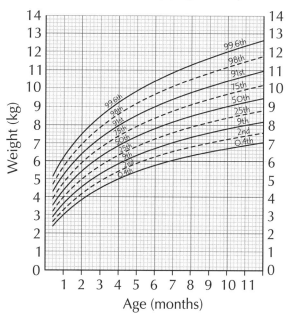

Growth chart for boys, aged 0-1 years

a) A four-month-old baby weighs 6.5 kg.
What percentile is the baby in?

.... percentile

b) In a sample of 600 four-month-old babies, how many would weigh 6.5 kg or less?

.... babies

c) A baby is in the 75th percentile for weight.
In a sample of 400 babies, how many would weigh more than this baby?

.... babies

Linear Graphs

A linear graph is a straight line graph. The variable on one axis increases or decreases along with the variable on the other axis — so this gives a straight line. You can write the line as an equation...

Example

The graph shows the volume of oxygen released in a chemical reaction over time.

Write the equation of the graph line in the form $y = mx + c$.

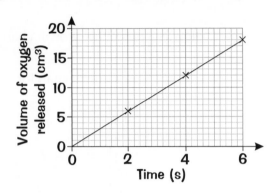

1 Find the *y*-intercept of the line — this is '*c*' in the equation.

The *y*-intercept is the point where the line crosses the *y*-axis.

The graph line crosses the *y*-axis at O. So the *y*-intercept is O.

The *x*-intercept is where the line crosses the *x*-axis.

2 Find the gradient of the line — this is '*m*' in the equation.
Calculate the gradient by dividing the change in *y* by the change in *x*: gradient = $\dfrac{\text{change in } y}{\text{change in } x}$

Pick two points on the line that are easy to read and a good distance apart.
Here, (2,6) and (6,18) are easy to read.

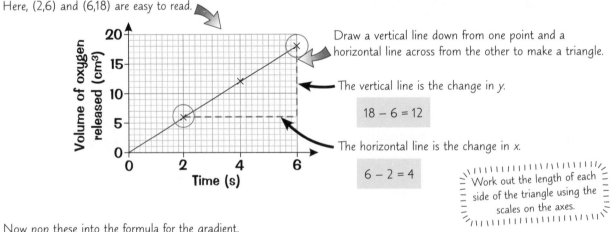

Draw a vertical line down from one point and a horizontal line across from the other to make a triangle.

The vertical line is the change in *y*.

$18 - 6 = 12$

The horizontal line is the change in *x*.

$6 - 2 = 4$

Work out the length of each side of the triangle using the scales on the axes.

Now pop these into the formula for the gradient.

gradient = $\dfrac{\text{change in } y}{\text{change in } x}$ gradient = $\dfrac{12}{4} = 3$ So the gradient is 3.

3 Put it all together in the $y = mx + c$ equation.

The gradient (*m*) is 3.

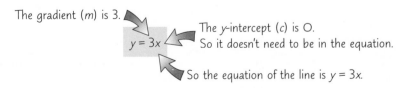

$y = 3x$

The *y*-intercept (*c*) is O.
So it doesn't need to be in the equation.

So the equation of the line is $y = 3x$.

Linear Graphs

Your go now at some questions on linear graphs. If, by the end of the page, you're sick of straight lines, draw a big squiggly one. (I'd advise getting a sheet of scrap paper, rather than using the wall.)

Q1 The graph below shows how the amount of carbon dioxide produced changes during the first 40 seconds of a reaction.

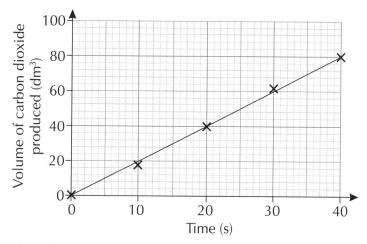

a) Give the value of the *y* intercept.

....

b) Calculate the gradient of the line.

....

c) Write the equation of the graph line in the form $y = mx + c$.

....

Q2 The graph shows how the temperature of a reaction changed over time. Write the equation of the graph line in the form $y = mx + c$.

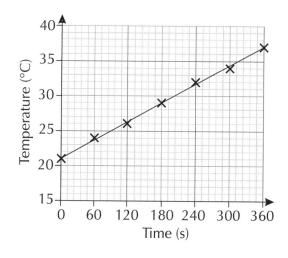

....

Section 3 — Analysing Data

Using Tangents

Knowing how to work out gradients is really important — it's how to find the rate of a reaction.
You learnt how to work out the gradient of a line on page 58. However, not all graphs are straight lines
— luckily, you can use a clever technique if you need to work out the gradient for a curved line.

Example

The graph on the right shows the change in
concentration of a reactant during the first
6 minutes of an experiment.

Calculate the rate of reaction after 2 minutes.

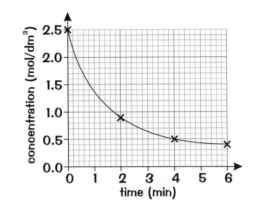

① Find the point on the curve that
you're interested in.

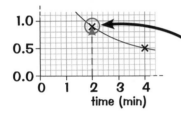

The question asks about the rate of the reaction after 2 minutes.
Find 2 on the x-axis and draw a line up to the curve from there.

② Place a ruler at the point you're interested in so that it's just touching the curve.

Position the ruler so you
can see the whole curve.

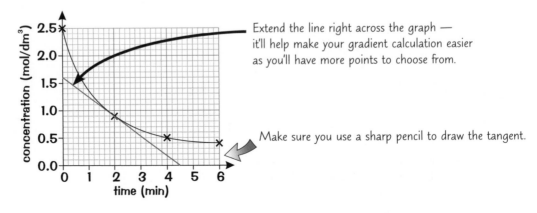

Adjust the ruler until the space
between the ruler and the curve is
equal on both sides of the point.

③ Draw a line along the ruler to make the tangent.

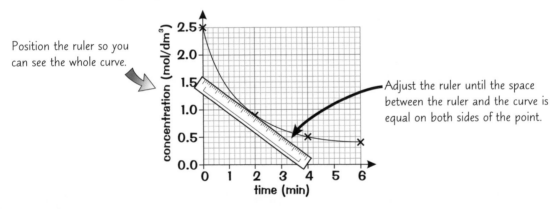

Extend the line right across the graph —
it'll help make your gradient calculation easier
as you'll have more points to choose from.

Make sure you use a sharp pencil to draw the tangent.

4 Calculate the gradient of the tangent.

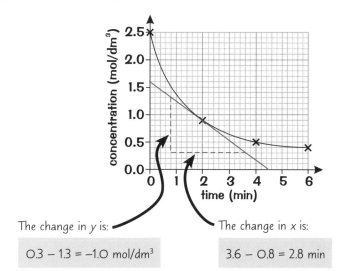

The change in y is:

0.3 − 1.3 = −1.0 mol/dm³

The change in x is:

3.6 − 0.8 = 2.8 min

Remember, gradient = $\frac{\text{change in } y}{\text{change in } x}$

gradient = $\frac{-1.0}{2.8}$ = −0.35714... = −0.36 (2 s.f.)

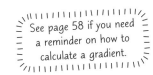
See page 58 if you need a reminder on how to calculate a gradient.

5 Work out the correct units for the rate by putting the units that you know into the gradient formula.

The change in y is the change in concentration, given in mol/dm³.

Gradient = $\frac{\text{change in } y}{\text{change in } x}$ = $\frac{\text{mol/dm}^3}{\text{min}}$ = mol/dm³/min

Change the dividing line in the formula to a '/' in the unit.

The change in x is the change in time, given in minutes.

6 Put the value and the unit together to get the rate of reaction.

rate = 0.36 mol/dm³/min (to 2 s.f.)

The gradient you've calculated (−0.36) is the value of the rate.

The gradient is negative, but rate of reaction is always given as a positive value, so you can ignore the minus sign for the final answer here.

7 Do the hokey cokey.

Section 3 — Analysing Data

Using Tangents

There are a few steps to getting the answers to these questions, but just work through them carefully and you'll get there. You'll need a ruler, so if you haven't got one, go and grab one. And maybe a cuppa too.

Q1   The graph shows the change in concentration of a product during the first six minutes of a reaction. Calculate the rate of the reaction after 2 minutes.

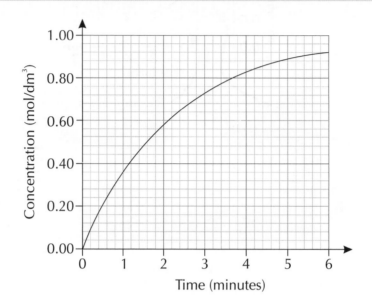

.... mol/dm³/min

Q2   The graph below shows how far a cyclist travels over 35 seconds. Calculate the rate that the cyclist is travelling at 20 seconds.

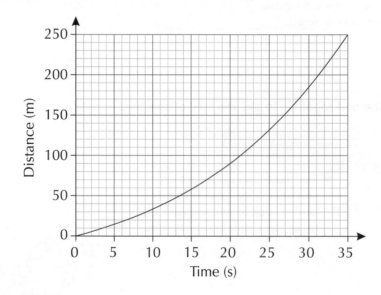

.... m/s

Section 3 — Analysing Data

Q3 The graph below shows how far a train travels plotted against time. Calculate the rate that the train is travelling one hour into the journey. Include the units for the rate in your answer.

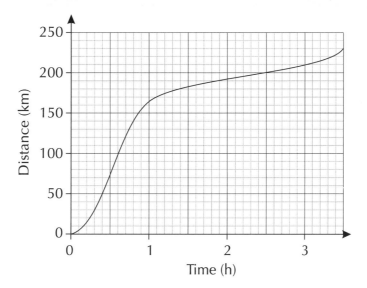

.... units: ....

Q4 The graph shows the change in concentration of a product over time during a chemical reaction. Calculate the rate of the reaction at 30 seconds. Include the units for the rate in your answer.

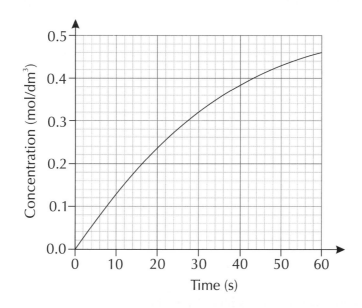

.... units: ....

Section 3 — Analysing Data

Distance-Time Graphs — Calculating Speed

Distance-time graphs show you exactly that — distance travelled and time taken. The gradient (the slope) of a distance-time graph is equal to the speed the object is going. Pretty nifty if you ask me.

Example

Joe was driving home along a straight road. Below is a distance-time graph of the start of his journey. Calculate the speed he was travelling at between 15 and 40 seconds.

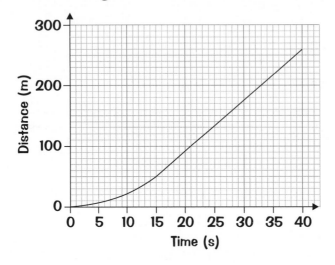

1 Work out the distance he travelled between 15 and 40 seconds.

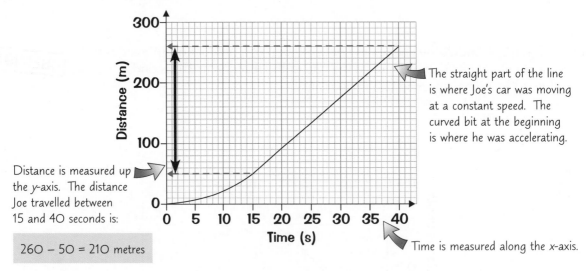

The straight part of the line is where Joe's car was moving at a constant speed. The curved bit at the beginning is where he was accelerating.

Distance is measured up the y-axis. The distance Joe travelled between 15 and 40 seconds is:

260 − 50 = 210 metres

Time is measured along the x-axis.

2 Work out the time taken.

You're given the numbers in the question, so: 40 seconds − 15 seconds = 25 seconds

3 Divide the distance he travelled by the time it took him. This gives you the gradient, which is the speed.

You may have seen this before with this equation:
$$\text{Speed} = \frac{\text{Distance}}{\text{Time}}$$

210 m ÷ 25 s = 8.4 m/s

The distance travelled.

The time taken.

This is his speed.
The units are m/s because the distance was measured in metres and the time was measured in seconds.

Distance-Time Graphs — Calculating Speed

Being able to calculate a gradient is pretty important with these graphs. See how you get on with this lot...

Q1   Rajni walked the length of a road. She rested for two minutes then jogged back to her start point, as shown in the graph below.

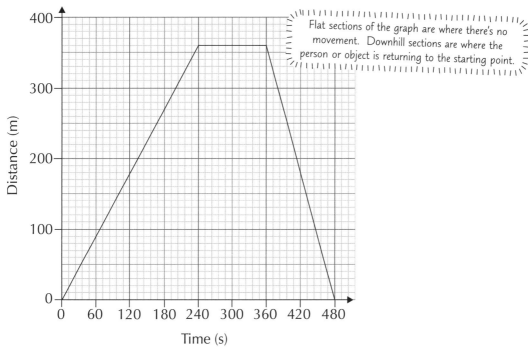

Flat sections of the graph are where there's no movement. Downhill sections are where the person or object is returning to the starting point.

a)   What was her speed as she walked to the end of the road?

.... m/s

b)   At what speed did she jog back to the start point?

.... m/s

Q2   The distance-time graph below shows the distance a bus travelled from its starting point plotted against time. What was its speed between 30 and 50 seconds?

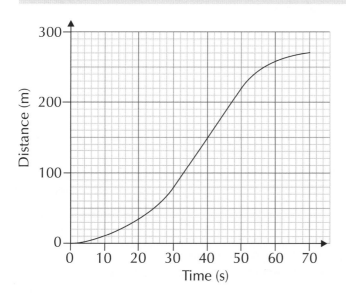

.... m/s

Section 3 — Analysing Data

Velocity-Time Graphs — Calculating Acceleration

Velocity is speed with a direction. When it's plotted against time on a graph, you can use it to calculate the acceleration of an object, since the acceleration is equal to the gradient of the line. And here's how...

Example

On the right is a velocity-time graph of a car travelling along a straight road.

What is its acceleration between 10 and 20 seconds?

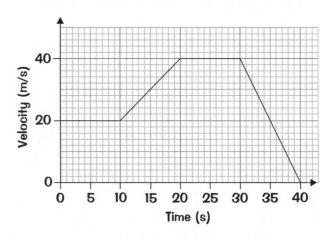

1 Work out the change in velocity by subtracting the initial velocity from the final velocity.

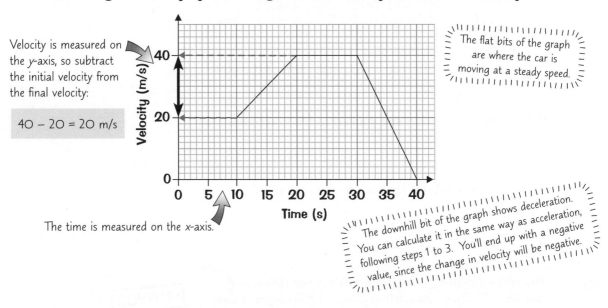

Velocity is measured on the *y*-axis, so subtract the initial velocity from the final velocity:

40 – 20 = 20 m/s

The time is measured on the *x*-axis.

The flat bits of the graph are where the car is moving at a steady speed.

The downhill bit of the graph shows deceleration. You can calculate it in the same way as acceleration, following steps 1 to 3. You'll end up with a negative value, since the change in velocity will be negative.

2 Work out the time taken for the change in velocity.

You've been given the numbers you need in the question, so:

20 seconds – 10 seconds = 10 seconds

3 Divide the change in velocity by the time taken to get the gradient — that's the acceleration.

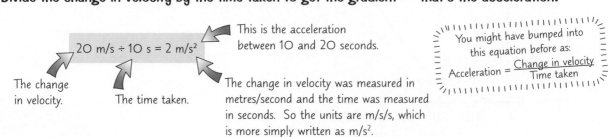

20 m/s ÷ 10 s = 2 m/s²

This is the acceleration between 10 and 20 seconds.

The change in velocity.

The time taken.

The change in velocity was measured in metres/second and the time was measured in seconds. So the units are m/s/s, which is more simply written as m/s².

You might have bumped into this equation before as:

$$\text{Acceleration} = \frac{\text{Change in velocity}}{\text{Time taken}}$$

Velocity-Time Graphs — Calculating Acceleration

Learning how to calculate gradients can be a bit of an uphill struggle. But never fear — here are some lovely velocity-time graphs for you to put that learning into practice.

Q1 The graph below shows the velocity of a cyclist plotted against time. What is the cyclist's acceleration between 2 and 5 seconds?

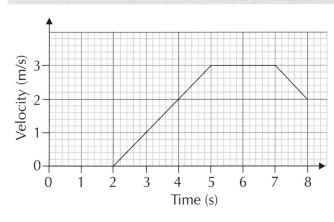

.... m/s^2

Q2 A race car accelerates to 50 m/s. Calculate its acceleration between 3 and 6 seconds from the velocity-time graph below.

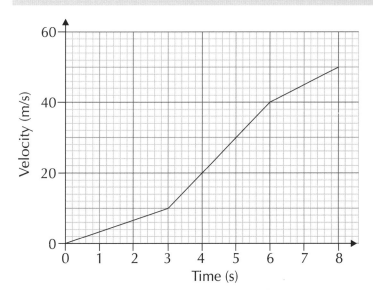

.... m/s^2

Q3 A ball rolls across a flat surface until it comes to a stop. What is its deceleration?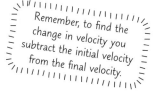

Remember, to find the change in velocity you subtract the initial velocity from the final velocity.

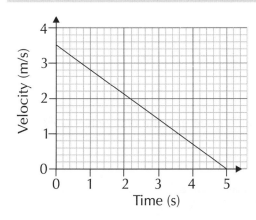

.... m/s^2

HIGHER Velocity-Time Graphs — Calculating Distance

Velocity-time graphs can also be used to calculate the distance an object travels in a given time.
No gradients needed this time — now it's all about the area underneath the graph.

Example

On the right is a velocity-time graph of
a car travelling along a straight road.

What is the total distance it travelled
between 20 and 30 seconds?

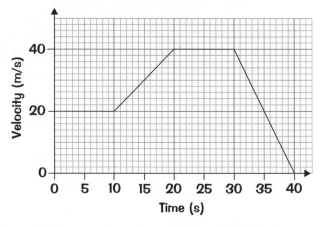

1 You need to work out the area under the graph for the time period mentioned in the question.
So first, work out the width of the bit you're interested in.

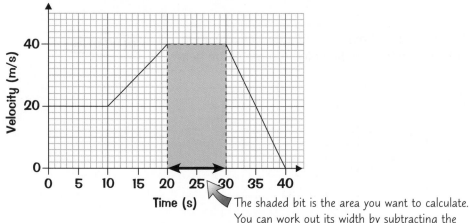

The shaded bit is the area you want to calculate.
You can work out its width by subtracting the
smaller x-axis value from the larger value.

$30 - 20 = 10 \text{ s}$

2 Next, work out the height of the bit you're interested in.

You can work out the
height of the shaded
area by reading it from
the y-axis. Easy.
Here it's 40 m/s.

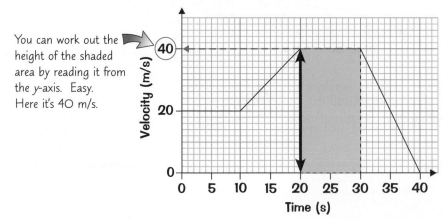

3 Multiply the width by the height to get the area — which gives you the distance travelled.

$10 \text{ s} \times 40 \text{ m/s} = 400 \text{ m}$

This is the distance travelled
between 20 and 30 seconds.

Example

The graph on the right is a velocity-time graph of a person cycling.

Estimate how far the person cycled in the first 10 seconds.

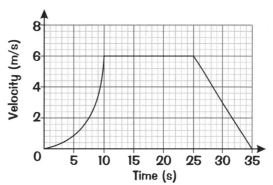

1 Work out which bit of the graph you're interested in.

You just want the bit up to 10 seconds. So that's this shaded bit:

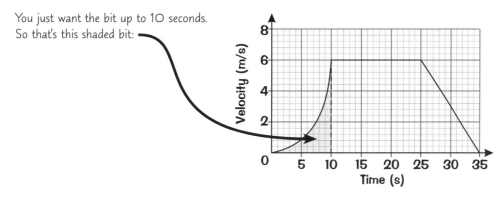

2 Work out the distance that each square on the grid represents.

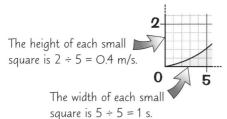

The height of each small square is 2 ÷ 5 = 0.4 m/s.

The width of each small square is 5 ÷ 5 = 1 s.

The area of one square is equal to the distance it represents. So the distance represented by one square in this graph is:

1 s × 0.4 m/s = 0.4 m

3 Count the number of squares in the bit of the graph you're interested in.

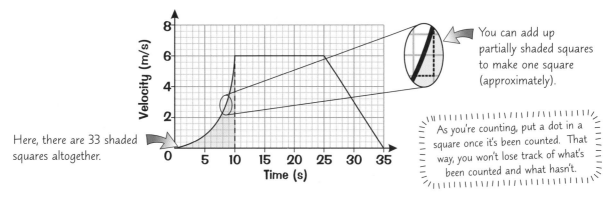

You can add up partially shaded squares to make one square (approximately).

Here, there are 33 shaded squares altogether.

As you're counting, put a dot in a square once it's been counted. That way, you won't lose track of what's been counted and what hasn't.

4 Multiply the distance that each square represents by the number of squares under the graph to find the total distance.

Each square represents 0.4 m.

0.4 × 33 = 13.2 m

So the total distance travelled in 10 s is 13.2 metres.

There are 33 shaded squares.

5 Another good use of squares...

Don't go spoiling your dinner now...

Velocity-Time Graphs — Calculating Distance

It's your turn now. Have a go at working out the distances from this new bunch of velocity-time graphs.

Q1 The graph below shows the velocity of a cyclist plotted against time. How far did the cyclist travel between 2 and 5 seconds?

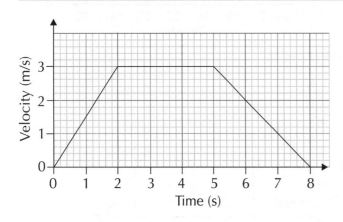

.... m

Q2 The graph below shows the velocity of a cyclist plotted against time. Estimate how far the cyclist travelled in the first 5 seconds.

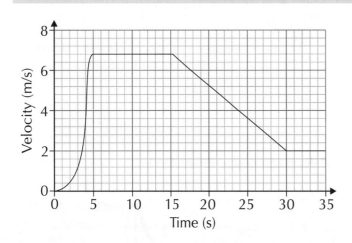

.... m

Q3 The graph below shows the velocity of a car plotted against time. Estimate how far the car travelled between 0 and 15 seconds.

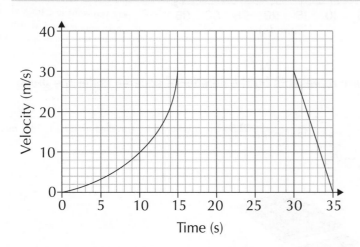

.... m

Q4 The graph below shows the velocity of a skydiver after she jumps out of a plane. After 40 seconds she opens her parachute — how far does she fall before then?

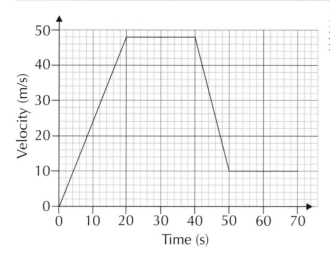

TIP: It'll be easier here if you split the area into two shapes. The area of a triangle is given by ½ x base x height.

.... m

Q5 The graph below shows the velocity of a car plotted against time. Did the car travel further between 0 and 10 seconds or between 20 and 35 seconds?

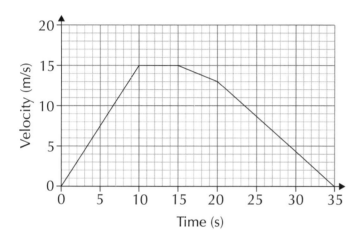

....

Q6 Lisa is running in a race at a steady velocity. When she sees the finish line, she accelerates until she crosses it 5 seconds later. How far did she run between the start of her acceleration and crossing the finish line?

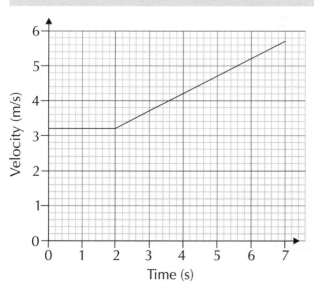

.... m

Section 3 — Analysing Data

Substituting Values into Formulas

If you can use one formula you can use them all. They can look a bit daunting at first — but once you substitute the letters or words for numbers, you're usually just a simple calculation away from the answer.

Example

The table on the right shows the results of a bike race. Work out the distance that Jenny cycled.

	Speed (m/s)	Time (min)
Jenny	5	3
Max	7	2

1 **Decide which formula you need to use.**

You know the speed and the time taken. You want to find out the distance Jenny travelled. So you need a formula that includes those three things.

The one you need here is: **distance (m) = speed (m/s) × time (s)**

There's a bunch of formulas that you'll just have to remember for the exams. Others will be given to you though. Make sure you know which ones you need to learn.

2 **Substitute the numbers from the question into the formula.**

distance = speed (m/s) × time (s)

Speed = 5 m/s
Time = 3 minutes
       = 3 × 60 = 180 seconds

So, distance = 5 m/s × 180 s

Make sure the numbers you're using are in the right units.

You need the time in seconds but you're given it in minutes in the table — you need to change it before you can put it in the formula.

3 **Calculate the answer.**

5 m/s × 180 s = 900 m

Don't forget to include the units in your answer.

4 **Take time to relax with some baking.**

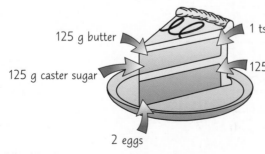

125 g butter

1 tsp vanilla extract

125 g caster sugar

125 g self-raising flour

2 eggs

Mix all the ingredients together then bake for about 20 minutes at 180 °C. When it's done, share with friends over homework and a cup of tea.

Substituting Values into Formulas

Now it's time for you to plug some numbers into these formulas. Keep an eye on those pesky units...

Q1 The speed of a wave can be calculated from its frequency and wavelength.

wave speed (m/s) = frequency (Hz) × wavelength (m)

a) A wave has a frequency of 2 Hz and a wavelength of 12 m. What is its wave speed?

.... m/s

b) What is the wave speed of a wave with a wavelength of 0.02 m and a frequency of 50 Hz?

.... m/s

Q2 A reaction with a theoretical yield of 42.1 g only made 35.4 g of product. What is the reaction's percentage yield?

$$\text{percentage yield (\%)} = \frac{\text{mass of product actually made (g)}}{\text{maximum theoretical mass of product (g)}} \times 100$$

.... %

Q3 Beth is 1.5 metres tall and has a body mass of 50 kg. What is her BMI?

$$\text{BMI} = \frac{\text{body mass (kg)}}{\text{height}^2 \text{(m)}}$$

....

Q4   A motor transfers 3.6 kJ of useful energy in 1.5 minutes.
What is its power output?

$$\text{power (W)} = \frac{\text{work done (J)}}{\text{time (s)}}$$

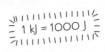

1 kJ = 1000 J

.... W

Q5   4.0 cm³ of blood passes through a section of a vein in 50 seconds.
Calculate the rate of blood flow through the vein.

$$\text{rate of blood flow (cm}^3\text{/min)} = \frac{\text{volume of blood (cm}^3)}{\text{time (min)}}$$

.... cm³/min

Q6   This table shows the force used to move two toy cars.
Calculate the work done in moving each car.

Car	Force (N)	Distance (cm)
A	5.00	157
B	10.00	223

work done (J) = force (N) × distance (m)

Car A: .... J

Car B: .... J

Q7 Jared added 25 cm³ of sodium hydroxide solution to completely neutralise an acid during a titration. He calculated that this volume contained 0.0025 moles of sodium hydroxide. What was the concentration of the sodium hydroxide solution?

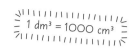
1 dm³ = 1000 cm³

$$\text{concentration (mol/dm}^3) = \frac{\text{number of moles}}{\text{volume (dm}^3)}$$

.... mol/dm³

Q8 A sheep weighing 44.5 kg stands at the top of a mountain that is 0.93 km high. The gravitational field strength is 9.8 N/kg. How much energy is in the sheep's gravitational potential energy store?

PHYSICS

gravitational potential energy (J) = mass (kg) × gravitational field strength (N/kg) × height (m)

.... J

Q9 The table below shows the masses of two cubes that are each made of a different material. Each cube has a volume of 64 cm³. Calculate the density of each cube.

1 m³ = 1 000 000 cm³

Cube	Mass (g)
A	172.8
B	32.0

$$\text{density (kg/m}^3) = \frac{\text{mass (kg)}}{\text{volume (m}^3)}$$

Cube A: .... kg/m³

Cube B: .... kg/m³

Section 4 — Algebra

Rearranging Formulas

Formulas are generally straightforward, but sometimes you have to rearrange them before they're of any use. Don't panic though — there are just a few simple steps to follow to get everything swapped about.

Example   A car is travelling at 6 m/s.
It accelerates at a rate of 1.54 m/s² for 2.6 seconds.
What is its final velocity?

1 **Decide which formula you need to use.**

You know the acceleration, the time and the car's initial velocity. You want to find out its final velocity. So you need to find a formula that includes those four things.

The one you want here is: $a = \dfrac{v - u}{t}$ a stands for acceleration, v stands for final velocity, u stands for initial velocity, and t stands for time.

2 **Decide what you need to make the subject.**

You need to find out the final velocity so you need to get v on its own.

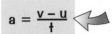

$a = \dfrac{v - u}{t}$

3 **Rearrange the formula. You should always do the same thing to each side. To get rid of something you need to do the opposite. Keep going until you have the thing you want on its own.**

$$a = \dfrac{v - u}{t}$$

The opposite of ÷t is ×t, so multiply both sides by t.

$(\times t)$ $a \times t = \dfrac{v - u}{t} \times t$

$a \times t = v - u$

The opposite of −u is +u, so add u to both sides.

$(+ u)$ $(a \times t) + u = v - u + u$

$(a \times t) + u = v$

$v = (a \times t) + u$ Switch the sides round so that v is at the front.

> The opposite of + is − and the opposite of − is +.
> The opposite of × is ÷ and the opposite of ÷ is ×.

4 **Now you can just substitute the numbers in, and calculate the answer.**

The acceleration (a) is 1.54 m/s².
Time (t) is 2.6 s.
The initial velocity (u) is 6 m/s.

$v = (a \times t) + u$
$v = (1.54 \times 2.6) + 6$
$v = \underline{10 \text{ m/s}}$ **(2 s.f.)**

You might need to round your answer to a sensible number of significant figures — see p.6 if you need a hand with that.

5 **Stroke a dog.**

Maybe not this one.

Rearranging Formulas

Right, your go. These formulas need a good swap about before you can answer the questions.

Q1   What is the mass of 4.2 moles of carbon ($A_r = 12$)?

TIP: you can use a formula triangle to help you rearrange a formula. If the formula you're using is $A = B \times C$, the triangle should look like this: ➔ All you do is put your finger over the bit you want and read off the formula. E.g. if you want to find B, you put your finger over that and it leaves behind $A \div C$.

$$\text{number of moles} = \frac{\text{mass (g)}}{A_r}$$

.... g

Q2   A lamp is connected to a 2 V battery. The power of the lamp is 0.8 W. Calculate the current flowing through the lamp.

power (W) = potential difference (V) × current (A)

.... A

Q3   A radio wave in a vacuum has a frequency of 95.4×10^6 Hz. The speed of all electromagnetic waves in a vacuum is 3.00×10^8 m/s. Calculate the wavelength of the radio wave.

wave speed (m/s) = frequency (Hz) × wavelength (m)

.... m

Q4 The real length of a bacterial cell is 6 µm. The cell is magnified by ×40. What is the length of the image?

$$\text{magnification} = \frac{\text{image size}}{\text{real size}}$$

.... µm

Q5 A spring has an extension of 2.5 cm when a force of 16 N is applied to it. Calculate the spring constant.

force (N) = spring constant (N/m) × extension (m)

.... N/m

Q6 A student dissolved 0.04 kg of sodium chloride in water to make a solution. The concentration of the solution is 160 g/dm³. What volume of water did the student use?

[CHEMISTRY]

$$\text{concentration (g/dm}^3) = \frac{\text{mass of solute (g)}}{\text{volume of solution (dm}^3)}$$

.... dm³

Q7   Copper has a specific heat capacity (SHC) of 385 J/kg°C.

change in thermal energy (J) = mass (kg) × SHC (J/kg°C) × temperature change (°C)

a)   A copper pot gives out 40 kJ of energy as it cools from 76 °C to 34 °C.
What is the mass of the pot?

.... kg

b)   33 kJ of energy is used to heat a 6.5 kg lump of copper.
The copper starts off at 18 °C. What temperature will it reach?

.... °C

Q8   A car accelerates over 200 m from an initial velocity of 13.4 m/s
to a final velocity of 31.2 m/s. What is the car's acceleration?

final velocity^2 (m/s) – initial velocity^2 (m/s) = 2 × acceleration (m/s^2) × distance (m)

.... m/s^2

Q9   Phil has a BMI of 21.6. He has a body mass of 57 000 g. How tall is he?

$$BMI = \frac{\text{body mass (kg)}}{\text{height}^2 \text{(m)}}$$

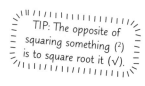

TIP: The opposite of squaring something (^{2}) is to square root it ($\sqrt{\ }$).

.... m

Area

Area is just the amount of space inside a shape. If the shape is drawn on a grid, you can roughly estimate its area by counting the squares inside it. Otherwise, you need to use a formula. The bad news is there's a different formula for each type of shape. The good news is three pretty useful ones are right here...

Example

A wildlife charity creates three different plans for a new nature reserve.
Calculate the area of each reserve.

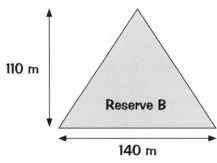
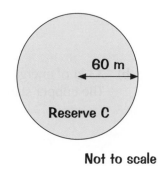

100 m   **Reserve A**   150 m

110 m   **Reserve B**   140 m

60 m   **Reserve C**

Not to scale

1 To find the area of a rectangle, use the formula: **area = length × width.**

Reserve A is a rectangle:

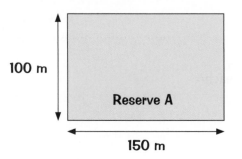

100 m

width

150 m

length

$150 \times 100 = 15\,000 \text{ m}^2$

So the area of Reserve A is 15 000 m².

Remember to include the units — the units of area are given in units squared.

2 To find the area of a triangle, use the formula: **area = $\frac{1}{2}$ × base × height.**

Reserve B is a triangle:

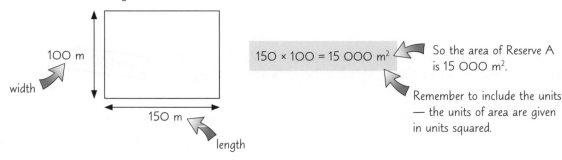

110 m

height

140 m

base

Make sure the measurement you use for the height is at right angles to the base.

$\frac{1}{2} \times 140 \times 110 = 7700 \text{ m}^2$

So the area of Reserve B is 7700 m².

3 To find the area of a circle, use the formula: **area = $\pi \times$ radius².**

Reserve C is a circle:

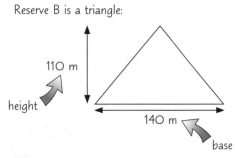

The radius of a circle is half the diameter (the distance across the circle through the middle).

60 m

You need to round this to 2 significant figures as that is all you are given in the question.

π (pi) is just a number a bit bigger than 3. If you don't have a button for it on your calculator, you can use the value 3.14.

$\pi \times 60^2 = 11\,309.73...$
$= 11\,000 \text{ m}^2 \text{ (2 s.f.)}$

So the area of Reserve C is 11 000 m².

Area

It's time to put those formulas into use and work out some areas. A calculator will definitely be handy...

Q1 A student is using two pieces of aluminium foil in an experiment. The pieces are shown below. Which piece has the largest area?

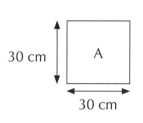

30 cm   A   30 cm

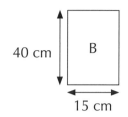

40 cm   B   15 cm   Not to scale

....

Q2 A student is investigating the amount of pressure applied to her thumb when she presses on a drawing pin. To do this, she needs to work out the area of the head of the drawing pin. The diameter of the head is 11 mm. Calculate the area.

11 mm

TIP: the diameter is two times the radius.

.... mm²

Q3 Ellis is looking at a root hair cell under a microscope. The diagram below shows the dimensions of the cell. Estimate the area of the cell.

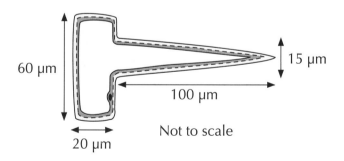

60 μm   15 μm   100 μm   20 μm   Not to scale

TIP: try breaking the cell into two separate shapes and then adding the areas together.

.... μm²

Section 5 — Geometry and Angles

Surface Area and Volume

Not all shapes are flat, so straight up area doesn't always tell you the whole story. Sometimes you need to find the surface area of a 3D shape. It's not as tricky as it sounds though — you can just break the shape down into its surfaces. Finding the volume isn't too bad either. There's just another formula to learn.

Example

A cell can be represented by a cuboid that measures 5 μm by 2 μm by 1 μm.

Work out:

a) the surface area

b) the volume

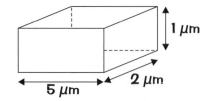

First, focus on part a)...

1 Break the shape down into flat surfaces and work out the area of each one.

See page 80 for a reminder of how to work out area.

A cuboid that measures 5 μm by 2 μm by 1 μm has six surfaces:

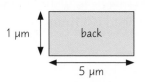

For the front and back: area = 5 μm × 1 μm = 5 μm²

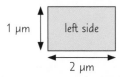

For the two sides: area = 2 μm × 1 μm = 2 μm²

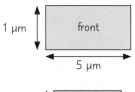

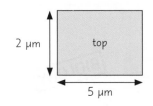

For the top and bottom: area = 5 μm × 2 μm = 10 μm²

2 Add up the areas of all the flat surfaces

5 + 5 + 2 + 2 + 10 + 10 = 34 μm²

So the total surface area of the cell is 34 μm².

Now for part b)...

1 To find the volume of a cuboid, use the formula: volume = length × width × height.

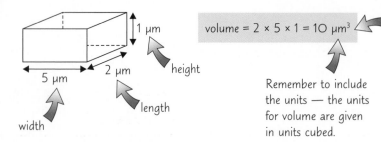

volume = 2 × 5 × 1 = 10 μm³

So the volume of the cell is 10 μm³.

Remember to include the units — the units for volume are given in units cubed.

You can use a similar method to find the volume of 3D shapes that aren't cuboids. You just find the area of the shape that you get when you cut through the object (the cross-section) and then multiply that by the length.

Surface Area and Volume

There are shapes waiting, so it be would be rude not to calculate their surface area and volume.

Q1 A student is investigating the densities of several solid objects. One of these objects is a wooden cube. The diagram on the right shows the dimensions of the cube.

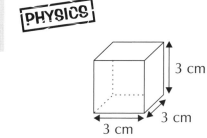

PHYSICS

3 cm
3 cm
3 cm

  a) Calculate the surface area of the cube.

.... cm²

  b) Calculate the volume of the cube.

.... cm³

Q2 A student is investigating the effect of surface area on the rate of reaction. She uses two different sizes of marble chips. A diagram of one of the large chips is shown on the right.

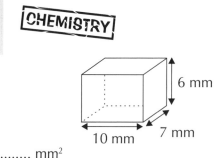

CHEMISTRY

6 mm
10 mm 7 mm

  a) Calculate the surface area of the marble chip.

.... mm²

  b) Calculate the volume of the marble chip.

.... mm³

Q3 A scientist is looking at the surface area to volume ratios of different organisms. On the right is a model of single-celled organism.

BIOLOGY

  a) Calculate the surface area of the organism.

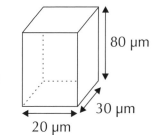

80 µm
30 µm
20 µm

.... µm²

  b) Calculate the volume of the organism.

.... µm³

Section 5 — Geometry and Angles

Measuring Angles

Sometimes examiners are lazy and don't label the angles in their diagrams. If that happens, you might just have to measure them yourself. This is all good if you have a protractor and you're not afraid to use it. Follow these steps and you'll know exactly what to do.

Example

The diagram on the right shows a ray of light hitting a mirror.
Use a protractor to measure angle *x*.

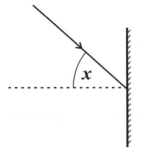

1 First line up the mark in the centre of the protractor with the point of the angle.
Then line up the baseline of the protractor with the lower line that forms the angle.

Line up the dotted line
with the baseline here.

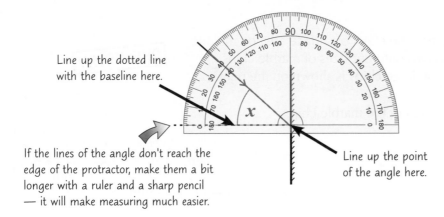

If the lines of the angle don't reach the edge of the protractor, make them a bit longer with a ruler and a sharp pencil — it will make measuring much easier.

Line up the point
of the angle here.

2 Read off the value on the scale of the protractor where the other line of the angle meets it. This will give you the size of the angle.

The line crosses the scale
of the protractor at 40.
Each mark on the
protractor is 1°,
so angle *x* is 40°.

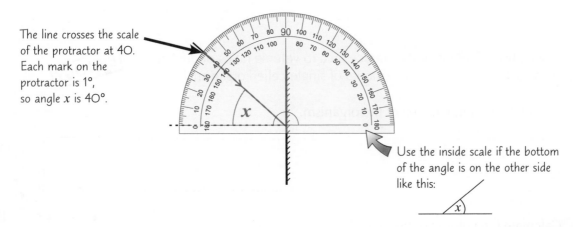

Use the inside scale if the bottom
of the angle is on the other side
like this:

3 Measure out 180° of pie and eat it.

Measuring Angles

No point hanging around — these angles won't measure themselves. Protractors at the ready...

Q1 A student shines a light at a mirror. The light ray hits the mirror at angle **B**. Use a protector to measure angle **B**.

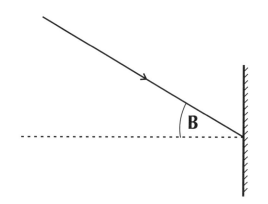

..................................°

Q2 The diagram below shows a ray of light hitting a surface. Use a protractor to measure angle **A**.

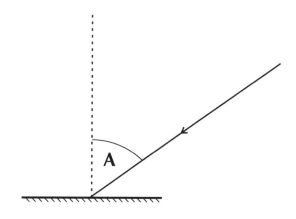

..................................°

Q3 A student is using a ray box to investigate the reflective properties of different surfaces. Use a protractor to measure the angle of reflection, **R**.

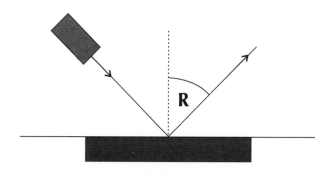

..................................°

Section 5 — Geometry and Angles

Scale Drawings

Scale drawings are accurate drawings of what is happening in real life, but they're just a bit smaller.
You can use them to find an overall (resultant) force by drawing the individual forces acting on an object.
You can also use them to split up a resultant force so you can measure its components. How exciting...

Example

A man is on an electric bicycle that has a driving force of 4 N east. However, the wind
produces a force of 3 N north. Find the magnitude and direction of the resultant force.

1 Choose a sensible scale for your drawing.
Use it to draw the forces that are acting, tip to tail.

The scale you choose needs to be easy
but it also needs to big enough so that
you can measure things accurately.

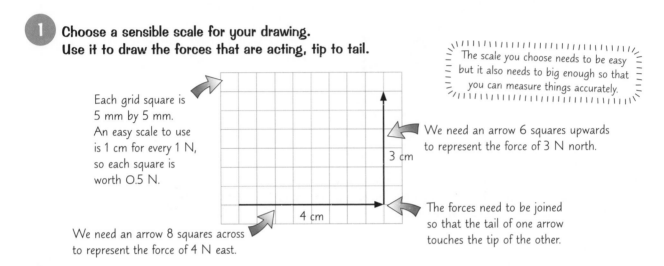

Each grid square is
5 mm by 5 mm.
An easy scale to use
is 1 cm for every 1 N,
so each square is
worth 0.5 N.

We need an arrow 6 squares upwards
to represent the force of 3 N north.

3 cm

4 cm

The forces need to be joined
so that the tail of one arrow
touches the tip of the other.

We need an arrow 8 squares across
to represent the force of 4 N east.

2 Draw a straight line from the tail of the first arrow to the tip of the last arrow — this is the resultant
force. Measure the length of this line with a ruler and use the scale to find the force in N.

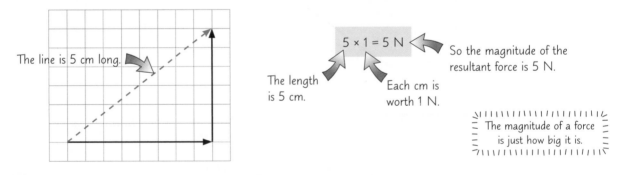

The line is 5 cm long.

5 × 1 = 5 N

So the magnitude of the
resultant force is 5 N.

The length
is 5 cm.

Each cm is
worth 1 N.

The magnitude of a force
is just how big it is.

3 Use a protractor to measure the direction of the force as a bearing.

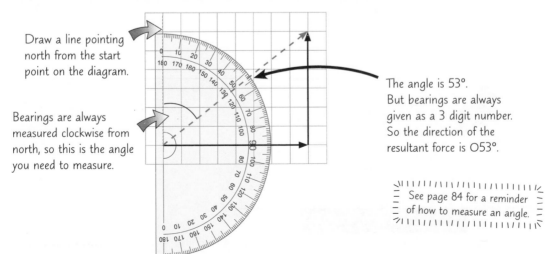

Draw a line pointing
north from the start
point on the diagram.

Bearings are always
measured clockwise from
north, so this is the angle
you need to measure.

The angle is 53°.
But bearings are always
given as a 3 digit number.
So the direction of the
resultant force is 053°.

See page 84 for a reminder
of how to measure an angle.

Section 5 — Geometry and Angles

Example

The scale diagram on the right shows a toy car being pulled along horizontally by a string. The tension in the string has a magnitude of **2.5 N**. Find the magnitude of this force acting in the direction of the car's motion.

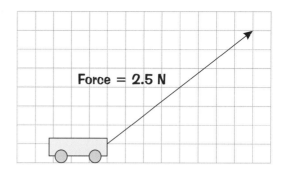

Force = 2.5 N

1 Use a ruler to measure the length of the arrow.

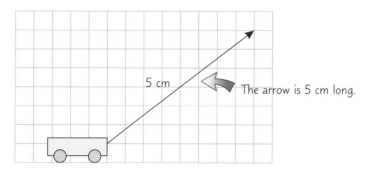

5 cm — The arrow is 5 cm long.

2 Divide the magnitude of the resultant force by the length to work out the scale used in the diagram.

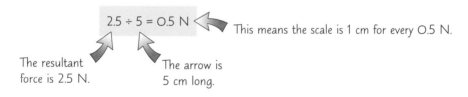

2.5 ÷ 5 = 0.5 N — This means the scale is 1 cm for every 0.5 N.

The resultant force is 2.5 N. The arrow is 5 cm long.

3 Draw two arrows (one horizontal and one vertical) to join the tail of the arrow to the tip. Measure the length of the arrow that's pointing in the direction you're interested in.

The car is moving horizontally so you need to measure the horizontal arrow.

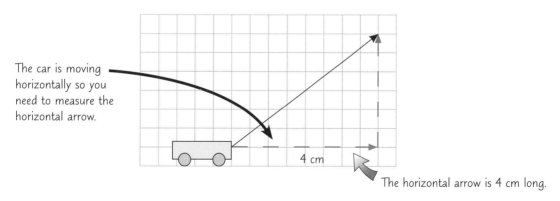

4 cm — The horizontal arrow is 4 cm long.

4 Work out the magnitude of the force by multiplying the arrow length by the scale used in the diagram.

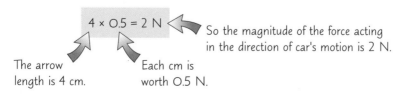

4 × 0.5 = 2 N — So the magnitude of the force acting in the direction of car's motion is 2 N.

The arrow length is 4 cm. Each cm is worth 0.5 N.

Section 5 — Geometry and Angles

Scale Drawings

These pages are like fish — they're covered in scales. Well, they will be once you've worked everything out.

Q1   The scale diagram below shows a tug boat pulling a barge out of a boat yard. The tension in the rope has a magnitude of 10 N. Find the magnitude of this force acting in the horizontal direction.

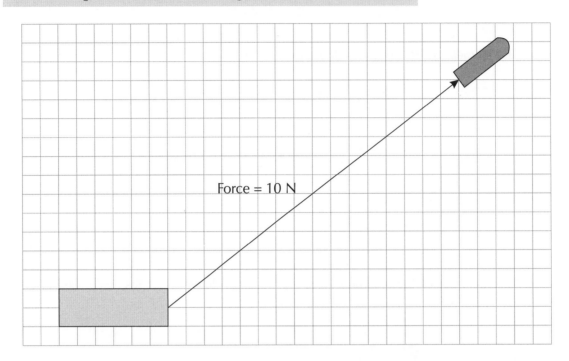

Force = 10 N

.... N

Q2   An object experiences a force of 6 N to the right and a force of 4 N downwards. Find the magnitude and direction of the resultant force.

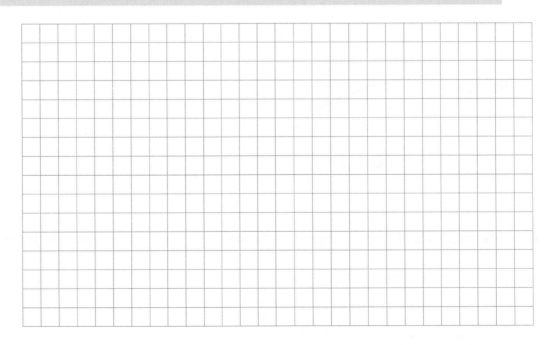

magnitude: .... N   direction: ....°

Section 5 — Geometry and Angles

Q3 The scale diagram below shows a force of 2.5 N acting at a bearing of 053°. Find the magnitude of this force acting in the vertical direction.

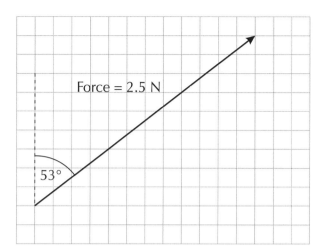

Force = 2.5 N

53°

.... N

Q4 A ferry is crossing a river with a driving force of 20 N east. However, the river is moving with a current of 8 N north. Find the magnitude and direction of the resultant force.

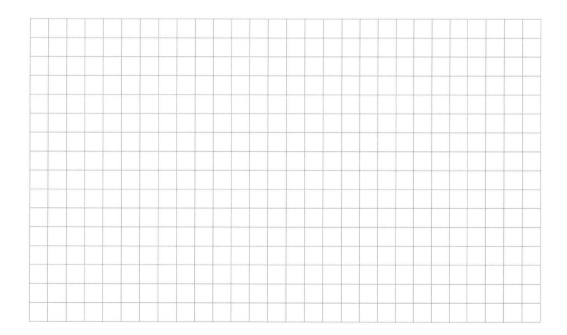

magnitude: .... N   direction: ....°

Section 5 — Geometry and Angles

Glossary

acceleration	How quickly an object's velocity is increasing.
anomalous result	A result that doesn't fit in with the rest of the results.
bar chart	A type of graph used to present discrete data or data that falls into categories. The height of a bar represents a quantity.
continuous data	Numerical data that can have any value within a range (e.g. length, volume or temperature).
correlation	A relationship between two variables (or a measure of how closely they're related).
deceleration	How quickly an object's velocity is decreasing.
dependent variable	The thing that's measured in an experiment.
directly proportional	A relationship between two variables where they both increase or decrease at the same rate.
discrete data	Numerical data that can only take certain values with no in-between value (e.g. number of people).
distance-time graph	A graph showing how the distance travelled by an object changes over a period of time.
fraction	A proportion that is written as one number over another. E.g. 1 out of 2 written as a fraction is ½.
gradient	The slope of a graph.
histogram	A type of graph used to present continuous data. The area of a bar represents a quantity.
independent variable	The thing you change in an experiment.
indirectly proportional	A relationship between two variables where one increases and the other decreases at the same rate. It can also be called inversely proportional.
line of best fit	A line on a graph which passes though or as near to as many points as possible.
linear graph	A straight line graph for which $y = mx + c$, where m = gradient and $c = y$ intercept.
mean	A measure of average for a set of results. It is calculated by adding together all of the data values and then dividing by the total number of values.
median	The middle value in a set of data that has been put in order of size.
mode	The most common value in a set of data.
negative correlation	A relationship where as one variable increases, the other variable decreases.

Glossary

origin	The point on a graph where both the x and y values are 0. It is written as (0,0).
percentage	A number written as an amount out of 100.
percentile	A value that shows the percentage of a data set that falls below it. E.g. if the 20th percentile height is 1.5 m, 20% of the data has a height less than 1.5 m.
pie chart	A round chart that is divided into sectors. The size of each sector shows the relative size of a quantity.
positive correlation	A relationship where as one variable increases, so does the other.
power	The number of times that a number is multiplied by itself.
probability	A measure of how likely something is to happen.
radius	The distance from the centre of a circle to its edge.
range	How spread out a set of results is. It is calculated by subtracting the smallest value from the largest value in a set of data.
ratio	A way of comparing two quantities. Ratios are written in the form $a : b$. E.g. a ratio of males to females of 1 : 2 would mean there were 2 females for every 1 male.
scatter diagram	A graph where the data is plotted as points. If a correlation is seen, a line of best fit can be drawn to show the relationship between the two variables.
significant figures (s.f.)	The digits in a number (in order, starting from the first non-zero digit).
standard form	A number written in the form $A \times 10^n$, where A is a number between 1 and 10.
tangent	A straight line that just touches a curve at a particular point but does not pass through it. It has the same gradient as the curve at that point.
uncertainty	The amount of error that a set of results might have.
variable	A factor in an investigation that can change or be changed (e.g. temperature or concentration).
velocity	How fast an object is travelling (its speed) in a specific direction.
velocity-time graph	A graph showing how the velocity of an object changes over a period of time.
x-axis	The axis that runs along the bottom of a graph.
x intercept	The point on a graph where the line crosses the x-axis.
y-axis	The axis that runs up the side of a graph.
y intercept	The point on a graph where the line crosses the y-axis.

Index

Answers

Section 1 — Calculations

Page 3 — Calculating the Mean and Range

1 Wire 1:
Mean = (5 + 4 + 6) ÷ 3 = 5 Ω
Range = 6 − 4 = 2 Ω

Wire 2:
Mean = (9 + 10 + 8) ÷ 3 = 9 Ω
Range = 10 − 8 = 2 Ω

2 Person A:
Mean = (0.04 + 0.08 + 0.05 + 0.07) ÷ 4 = 0.06 s
Range = 0.08 − 0.04 = 0.04 s

Person B:
Mean = (0.07 + 0.06 + 0.05 + 0.06) ÷ 4 = 0.06 s
Range = 0.07 − 0.05 = 0.02 s

Person C:
Mean = (0.05 + 0.04 + 0.04 + 0.07) ÷ 4 = 0.05 s
Range = 0.07 − 0.04 = 0.03 s

Person D:
Mean = (0.05 + 0.06 + 0.04) ÷ 3 = 0.05 s
Range = 0.06 − 0.04 = 0.02 s

The first repeat for Person D is an anomalous result so you should not include it in your calculations.

Page 5 — Calculating the Median and Mode

1 a) 21 dandelions
 b) 2, 8, 17, 20, 21, 21, 29
 20 dandelions

2 a) 16 s
 b) 12, 13 , 14, 16, 16, 17
 (14 + 16) ÷ 2 = 15 s

3 a) 0.03 m
 b) 0.03, 0.03, 0.03, 0.03, 0.05, 0.05, 0.06, 0.07
 (0.03 + 0.05) ÷ 2 = 0.04 m

Page 7 — Using Significant Figures

1 24.9 cm^3

2 2200 slugs

3 7160 kg/m^3

4 31 bubbles

Page 9 — Converting Units

1 14.2 ÷ 100 = 0.142 m

2 24 × 1000 = 24 000 mg

3 22 ÷ 1000 = 0.022 mm

4 2.2 × 1000 = 2200 W

5 75 000 ÷ 1000 = 75 kg
 169 ÷ 100 = 1.69 m

Page 11 — Using Standard Form

1 $1 × 10^{-3}$ mol/dm^3

2 $1.34 × 10^5$ dm^3

3 $1.25 × 10^{-3}$ mm

4 $3.39 × 10^6$ J

5 $1.2 × 10^{-4}$ m

Page 13 — Writing Ratios

1 1 : 3

2 15 : 25
 15 ÷ 5 = 3, 25 ÷ 5 = 5
 so ratio is 3 : 5.

3 6 : 12 : 6
 6 ÷ 6 = 1, 12 ÷ 6 = 2, 6 ÷ 6 = 1
 so ratio is 1 : 2 : 1.

4 2 : 4 : 12
 2 ÷ 2 = 1, 4 ÷ 2 = 2, 12 ÷ 2 = 6
 so ratio is 1 : 2 : 6.

Remember to pay attention to which way round your numbers should go.

5 6000 : 30 000
 6000 ÷ 6000 = 1, 30 000 ÷ 6000 = 5
 so ratio is 1 : 5.

You could also have simplified this ratio by making more, smaller divisions e.g. by dividing both sides by 6 and then 1000.
You should still have got the same answer.

Page 15 — Calculating Percentages and Fractions

1 10 + 9 + 5 + 6 = 30 g
 9 ÷ 30 = 0.3
 0.3 × 100 = 30%

2 95 400 ÷ 180 000 = 0.53
 0.53 × 100 = 53%

3 $\frac{27}{96} = \frac{9}{32}$

4 $\frac{36}{492} = \frac{9}{123} = \frac{3}{41}$

Page 17 — Probability

1 2 ÷ 4 = 0.5
 0.5 × 100 = 50%

2 $\frac{1}{4}$

3 a) 1 ÷ 4 = 0.25
 0.25 × 100 = 25%

 b) 25 ÷ 100 = 0.25
 0.25 × 12 = 3 offspring

Page 19 — Calculating Percentage Change

1    $\dfrac{14-11}{11} \times 100 = (3 \div 11) \times 100 = 27.2727...$
     $= 27\%$ (2 s.f.)

Remember to round your answer to the smallest number of significant figures used in the calculation.

2    $\dfrac{55-212}{212} = (-157 \div 212) \times 100 = -74\%$ (2 s.f.)

3   0.2 mol/dm³:
     $\dfrac{23.8-22.2}{22.2} = (1.6 \div 22.2) \times 100 = 7.21\%$ (3 s.f.)
     0.4 mol/dm³:
     $\dfrac{17.4-18.8}{18.8} = (-1.4 \div 18.8) \times 100 = -7.45\%$ (3 s.f.)

Page 21 — Making Estimates

1   The width fits into the length approximately 3 times. So the width is approximately $4.5 \div 3 = 1.5$ μm

2    $30\,000 \div 5 = 6000$ kg

3    $30 \times 10 = 300$ m

4    $3000 \times 10 = 30\,000$ dandelions

28 800 is close to 30 000, so Sabrina's answer is likely to be correct.

Page 23 — Calculating Sin x and Sin⁻¹ x

1    $n = \dfrac{\sin i}{\sin r} = \dfrac{\sin 21}{\sin 17} = 1.2$ (2 s.f.)

2    $n = \dfrac{\sin i}{\sin r} = \dfrac{\sin 27}{\sin 17} = 1.6$ (2 s.f.)

3    $\sin C = \dfrac{1}{n} = \dfrac{1}{1.44} = 0.6944...$
     $C = \sin^{-1} 0.6944... = 44.0°$ (3 s.f.)

4    $\sin r = \dfrac{\sin i}{n} = \dfrac{\sin 31}{1.36} = 0.378...$
     $\sin^{-1} 0.378... = 22°$ (2 s.f.)

Make sure your answers look sensible when you're calculating angles. If you come out with an answer of something like 495°, you've probably gone wrong somewhere.

Section 2 — Presenting Data

Page 25 — Drawing Tables

1

Temperature (°C)	Reaction time (s)		
	Repeat 1	Repeat 2	Repeat 3
10	31	30	29
20	22	19	20
30	10	11	11

2

Antibiotic	Space around antibiotic disc (mm)		
	Repeat 1	Repeat 2	Repeat 3
A	7	6	8
B	1	3	2

3

Parachute area (cm²)	Time taken to fall (s)			
	Repeat 1	Repeat 2	Repeat 3	Repeat 4
25	4.2	4.6	4.3	4.4
36	6.9	5.1	7.2	7.1
49	9.7	9.6	9.5	9.3

Page 27 — Using Frequency Tables

1

Heart rate	Tally	Frequency
160 - 164	II	2
165 - 169	III	3
170 - 174	II	2
175 - 179	IIII II	7
180 - 184	IIII I	6

2

pH	Tally	Frequency
3	IIII	5
4	I	1
5	I	1
6	I	1
7	I	1
8	IIII I	6
9	II	2
10	I	1
11	II	2

Pages 30-31 — Drawing Bar Charts

1

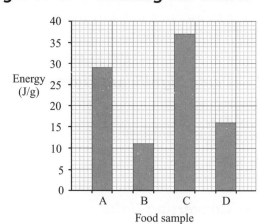

2

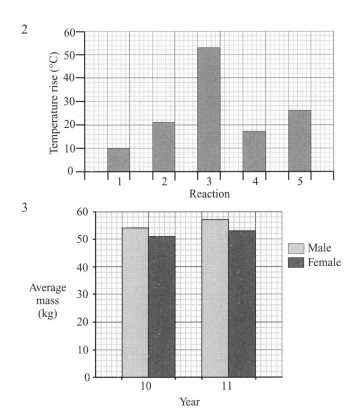

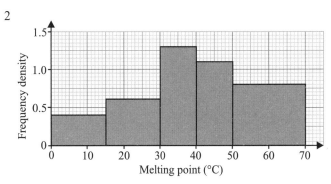

2

3

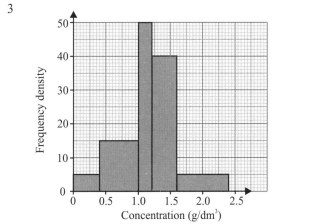

3

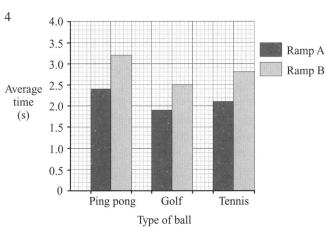

4

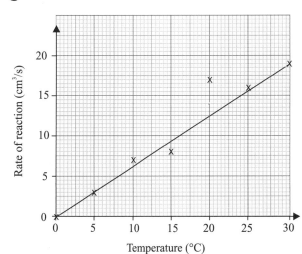

4

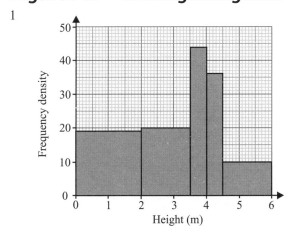

Pages 38-39 — *Drawing Scatter Diagrams*

1

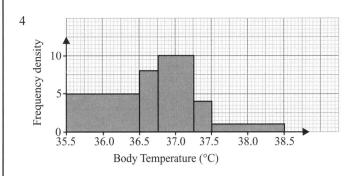

Pages 34-35 — *Drawing Histograms*

1

2

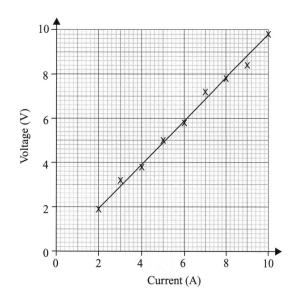

3

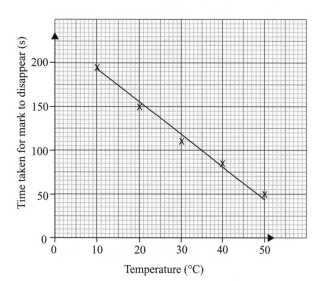

4

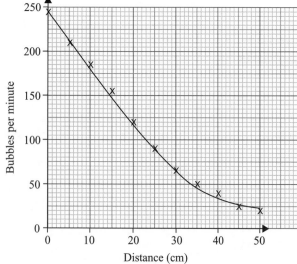

Page 41 — Uncertainties

1 Range for ramp A = 46 − 42 = 4
Uncertainty = 4 ÷ 2 = 2
Uncertainty of the mean for ramp A = 44 ± 2 cm/s

Range for ramp B = 30 − 24 = 6
Uncertainty = 6 ÷ 2 = 3
Uncertainty of the mean for ramp B = 27 ± 3 cm/s

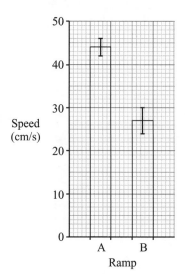

2 Range at 10 g/dm³ = 13 − 9 = 4
Uncertainty = 4 ÷ 2 = 2
Uncertainty of the mean at 10 g/dm³ = 11 ± 2 °C

Range at 20 g/dm³ = 17 − 15 = 2
Uncertainty = 2 ÷ 2 = 1
Uncertainty of the mean at 20 g/dm³ = 16 ± 1 °C

Range at 30 g/dm³ = 23 − 17 = 6
Uncertainty = 6 ÷ 2 = 3
Uncertainty of the mean at 30 g/dm³ = 20 ± 3 °C

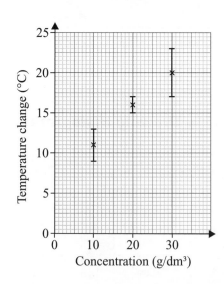

Section 3 — Analysing Data

Page 43 — Reading Tables

1 a) Catalyst A
  b) 17.5 – 4.5 = 13 cm³/s
2 a) Coal
  b) 920 – 440 = 480 g
3 a) 7.5 + 6.5 + 8.0 = 22 tonnes
  b) 8.0 + 5.0 = 13 tonnes

Page 45 — Using Pie Charts

1   50 + 5 + 16 + 6 + 15 = 92%
     100 – 92 = 8%

Remember, the whole pie chart should add up to 100%.

2 a) 36 + 2 + 13 = 51%
     100 – 51 = 49%
  b) 36 ÷ 100 = 0.36
     0.36 × 900 = 324 patients

Pages 48-49 — Interpreting Bar Charts

1   Sample C
2   51 – 14 = 37 g per 100 g
3   A: 120 – 86 = 34
     B: 125 – 110 = 15
     So, 34 – 15 = 19 g
4   100 – 44 – 31 – 8 = 17%

Page 51 — Interpreting Histograms

1   5 × 1.4 = 7
2   15 × 0.4 = 6
     10 × 1.5 = 15
     5 × 2.0 = 10
     Total students = 6 + 15 + 10 = 31
3   5 × 1.4 = 7
     5 × 1.2 = 6
     10 × 0.5 = 5
     Total samples = 7 + 6 + 5 = 18

Page 53 — Understanding Correlation

1   E.g. the graph shows a positive correlation. As the concentration increases, the change in temperature also increases.
2   E.g. the graph shows a negative correlation. As the temperature increases, the average number of bees in the area decreases.

Page 55 — Understanding Proportion

1   indirect (inverse) proportion
2   direct proportion

Page 57 — Percentiles

1 a) 25th percentile
  b) 25 ÷ 100 = 0.25
     0.25 × 600 = 150 babies
  c) 100% – 75% = 25%
     25 ÷ 100 = 0.25
     0.25 × 400 = 100 babies

In part c, you need to work out 25% of the sample, because you're looking at the number of babies above the 75th percentile.

Page 59 — Linear Graphs

1 a) 0
  b) change in y = 80 – 40 = 40
     change in x = 40 – 20 = 20
     gradient = 40 ÷ 20 = 2
  c) $y = 2x$

You might choose to use different points on the line, so your values for the change in y and the change in x might be different. You should get the same gradient though.

2   y-intercept = 21
     change in y = 37 – 21 = 16
     change in x = 360 – 0 = 360
     gradient = 16 ÷ 360 = 0.044 (2 s.f.)
     So equation of line is $y = 0.044x + 21$

Pages 62-63 — Using Tangents

1
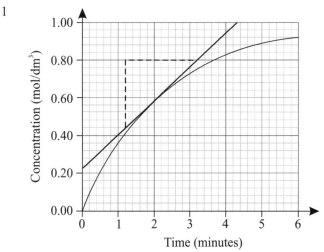
     change in y = 0.80 – 0.44 = 0.36
     change in x = 3.2 – 1.2 = 2.0
     rate = 0.36 ÷ 2.0 = 0.18 mol/dm³/min

Depending on how your draw your tangent, and which points you use, some of your working might be slightly different for these questions.

98

2

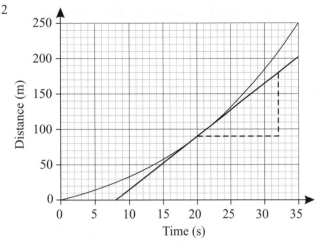

change in y = 180 – 90 = 90
change in x = 32 – 20 = 12
rate = 90 ÷ 12 = 7.5 m/s

3

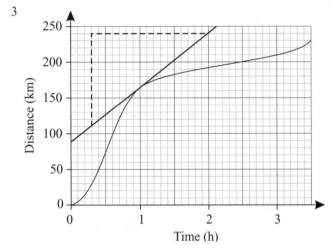

change in y = 240 – 110 = 130
change in x = 2.0 – 0.3 = 1.7
gradient = 130 ÷ 1.7 = 76.470... = 76 (2 s.f.)
units = km ÷ h = km/h
So the rate is 76 km/h.

4

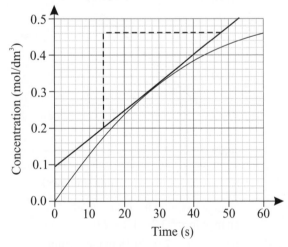

change in y = 0.46 – 0.20 = 0.26
change in x = 48 – 14 = 34
gradient = 0.26 ÷ 34 = 0.007647... = 0.0076 (2 s.f.)
units = mol/dm^3 ÷ s = mol/dm^3/s
So the rate is 0.0076 mol/dm^3/s.

Page 65 — Distance-Time Graphs — Calculating Speed

1 a) 360 m ÷ 240 s = 1.5 m/s
  b) 480 – 360 = 120 s
    360 m ÷ 120 s = 3 m/s
2   220 – 80 = 140 m
    140 m ÷ 20 s = 7 m/s

Page 67 — Velocity-Time Graphs — Calculating Acceleration

1   3 m/s ÷ 3 s = 1 m/s^2
2   Change in velocity = 40 – 10 = 30 m/s
    30 m/s ÷ 3 s = 10 m/s^2
3   –3.5 m/s ÷ 5 s = –0.7 m/s^2

Pages 70-71 — Velocity-Time Graphs — Calculating Distance

1   5 – 2 = 3 s
    3 s × 3 m/s = 9 m
2   Distance represented by 1 square = 1 s × 0.4 m/s
    = 0.4 m
    22 squares × 0.4 m = 8.8 m
3   Distance represented by 1 square = 1 s × 2 m/s = 2 m
    60 squares × 2 m = 120 m
4   It might make it simpler to break down the area under the graph into separate shapes first.
    Triangle: ½ × 20 s × 48 m/s = 480 m
    Rectangle: 40 – 20 = 20 s
    20 s × 48 m/s = 960 m
    Total distance = 480 + 960 = 1440 m
5   0-10 seconds:
    ½ × 10 s × 15 m/s = 75 m
    20-35 seconds:
    35 – 20 = 15 s
    ½ × 15 s × 13 m/s = 97.5 m
    So the car travelled further between 20-35 seconds.
6   Rectangle: 7 – 2 = 5 s
    5 s × 3.2 m/s = 16 m
    Triangle: 5.7 – 3.2 = 2.5 m/s
    ½ × 5 s × 2.5 m/s = 6.25 m
    Total distance = 16 + 6.25 = 22.25 m

Section 4 — Algebra

Pages 73-75 — Substituting Values into Formulas

1 a) 2 × 12 = 24 m/s
  b) 50 × 0.02 = 1 m/s

2    $(35.4 \div 42.1) \times 100 = 84.1\%$ (3 s.f.)

3    $50 \div 1.52 = 22$ (2 s.f.)

4   3.6 kJ $\times 1000 = 3600$ J
     1.5 minutes $\times 60 = 90$ s
     $3600 \div 90 = 40$ W

5   50 s $\div 60 = 0.8333333...$ min
     $4.0 \div 0.8333333... = 4.8$ cm^3/min

If possible, don't round any numbers until the end of your calculation. That way, you won't lose any accuracy in your answer.

6   Car A: $157 \div 100 = 1.57$ m
            $5.00 \times 1.57 = 7.85$ J
     Car B: $223 \div 100 = 2.23$ m
            $10.00 \times 2.23 = 22.3$ J

7   25 cm$^3 \div 1000 = 0.025$ dm^3
     $0.0025 \div 0.025 = 0.10$ mol/dm^3

8   0.93 km $\times 1000 = 930$ m
     $44.5 \times 9.8 \times 930 = 405\,573$ J

9   64 cm$^3 \div 1\,000\,000 = 0.000064$ m^3
     Cube A: 172.8 g $\div 1000 = 0.1728$ kg
             $0.1728 \div 0.000064 = 2700$ kg/m^3
     Cube B: 32.0 g $\div 1000 = 0.0320$ kg
             $0.0320 \div 0.000064 = 500$ kg/m^3

Pages 77-79 — Rearranging Formulas

1   mass = number of moles $\times A_r = 4.2 \times 12 = 50.4$ g

2    $\text{current} = \dfrac{\text{power}}{\text{potential difference}}$
     $= 0.8 \div 2 = 0.4$ A

3    $\text{wave length} = \dfrac{\text{wave speed}}{\text{frequency}}$
     $= (3.00 \times 10^8) \div (95.4 \times 10^6) = 3.14$ m (3 s.f.)

4   image size = magnification $\times$ real size
     $= 40 \times 6 = 240$ µm

5   2.5 cm $\div 100 = 0.025$ m
     $\text{spring constant} = \dfrac{\text{force}}{\text{extension}}$
     $= 16 \div 0.025 = 640$ N/m

6   0.04 kg $\times 1000 = 40$ g
     $\text{volume of solution} = \dfrac{\text{mass of solute}}{\text{concentration}}$
     $= 40 \div 160 = 0.25$ dm^3

7 a) 40 kJ $\times 1000 = 40\,000$ J
     temperature change $= 76 - 34 = 42$ °C
     $\text{mass} = \dfrac{\text{change in thermal energy}}{\text{SHC} \times \text{temperature change}}$
     $= 40\,000 \div (385 \times 42) = 2.5$ kg (2 s.f.)

  b) 33 kJ $\times 1000 = 33\,000$ J
     $\text{temperature change} = \dfrac{\text{change in thermal energy}}{\text{SHC} \times \text{mass}}$
     $= 33\,000 \div (385 \times 6.5) = 13$ °C (2 s.f.)
     $18 + 13 = 31$ °C

8    $\text{acceleration} = \dfrac{\text{final velocity}^2 - \text{initial velocity}^2}{2 \times \text{distance}}$
     $= (31.2^2 - 13.4^2) \div (2 \times 200)$
     $= 1.98$ m/s^2 (3 s.f.)

9    $57\,000$ g $\div 1000 = 57$ kg
     $\text{height}^2 = \dfrac{\text{body mass}}{\text{BMI}}$,
     $\text{height} = \sqrt{\dfrac{\text{body mass}}{\text{BMI}}}$
     $= \sqrt{(57 \div 21.6)}$
     $= 1.6$ m (2 s.f.)

Section 5 — Geometry and Angles

Page 81 — Area

1   Area of A $= 30 \times 30 = 900$ cm^2
     Area of B $= 40 \times 15 = 600$ cm^2
     So piece A has the largest area.

2   radius = diameter $\div 2 = 11 \div 2 = 5.5$
     Area $= \pi \times \text{radius}^2 = \pi \times 5.5^2 = 95.03...$
     $= 95$ mm^2 (2 s.f.)

3   Break the cell into a rectangle and a triangle:
     Area of rectangle $= 60 \times 20 = 1200$ µm^2
     Area of triangle $= 0.5 \times 15 \times 100 = 750$ µm^2
     Area of cell $= 1200 + 750 = 1950$ µm^2

Page 83 — Surface Area and Volume

1 a) Area of each surface $= 3 \times 3 = 9$ cm^2
     Total surface area $= 6 \times 9 = 54$ cm^2

  b) Volume $= 3 \times 3 \times 3 = 27$ cm^3

2 a) Area of top and bottom $= 10 \times 7 = 70$ mm^2
     Area of two sides $= 7 \times 6 = 42$ mm^2
     Area of front and back $= 10 \times 6 = 60$ mm^2
     Total surface area $= 70 + 70 + 42 + 42 + 60 + 60$
     $= 344$ mm^2

  b) Volume $= 10 \times 7 \times 6 = 420$ mm^3

3 a) Area of top and bottom $= 20 \times 30 = 600$ µm^2
     Area of two sides $= 30 \times 80 = 2400$ µm^2
     Area of front and back $= 20 \times 80 = 1600$ µm^2
     Total surface area $= 600 + 600 + 2400 + 2400 + 1600 + 1600 = 9200$ µm^2

  b) Volume $= 20 \times 30 \times 80 = 48\,000$ µm^3

Page 85 — Measuring Angles

1   Angle B $= 30°$

2   Angle A $= 55°$

3   Angle R $= 45°$

100

Pages 88-89 — Scale Drawings

1

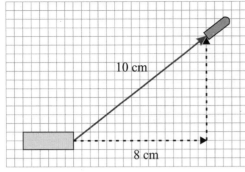

10 N ÷ 10 cm = 1, so scale = 1 cm for every 1 N.
magnitude = 8 × 1 = 8 N

2

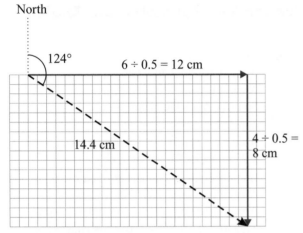

scale used: 1 cm = 0.5 N

magnitude = 14.4 × 0.5 = 7.2 N
direction = 124°

You could also use a 1 cm = 1 N scale but you should still get the same magnitude and direction.

3

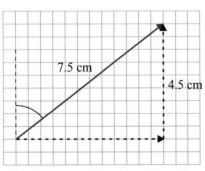

2.5 N ÷ 7.5 cm = $\frac{1}{3}$,
so scale = 1 cm for every $\frac{1}{3}$ N.

magnitude = 4.5 × $\frac{1}{3}$ = 1.5 N

4

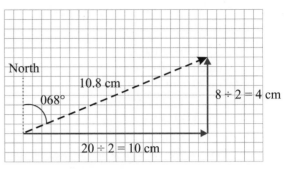

scale used: 1 cm = 2 N

magnitude = 10.8 × 2 = 21.6 N
direction = 068°

Answers